ch  ph  sh  th

C000184562

 aw ew  ow  ow wr

This **Letterland** book
belongs to:

....

 ar  or  er  ur  ir

 ai ea ee  oa

About this book

This *Letterland Beyond ABC Book* is the sequel to the *Letterland ABC Book*. It, too, transports young readers to the imaginary world of Letterland where letters spring to life and their sounds are taught in a unique story format. These brief, beautifully-illustrated stories give child-friendly reasons why, when certain letters come together, they make a completely new sound.

Whether at home or school, your children will quickly discover how easy it is to remember the new sound just by learning the story reason for it and having fun finding illustrated objects that contain the new sound. They'll also enjoy checking the Word List at the back of the book to see if they have spotted *all* the objects.

Harry Hat Man Stories		Walter Walrus Stories		The Robots' Stories		Vowel Men Stories	
ch	6-7 ✓	aw	16-17	ar	26-27	a e i o u	36-37
ph	8-9	ew	18-19	or	28-29	ai	38-39 ✓
sh	10-11 ✓	ow	20-21	er	30-31	ee	40-41
th	12-13	ow	22-23	ur	32-33	ea	42-43 ✓
wh	14-15	wr	24-25	ir	34-35	oa	43-44

The Letterland approach to teaching reading has been popular for over 25 years and meets research-based guidelines for teaching phonics. Best of all, each story is like a magic key to learning. It unlocks the new sound and makes it easy for children to read lots of other similar words - even if they've never seen them before! Have fun!

Published by Letterland International Ltd
33 New Road, Barton, Cambridge, CB23 7AY, UK

© Letterland International 2007

First published 2007. Reprinted 2008, 2010.
ISBN: 978-1-86209-398-0
Product Code: T99

12 11 10 9 8 7 6 5 4 3

LETTERLAND® is a registered trade mark of Lyn Wendon.

Written by Lisa Holt & Lyn Wendon
Educational Consultant: Lyn Wendon, originator of Letterland
Illustrated by Doreen Shaw
Design by Lisa Holt

Printed in Singapore

Letterland

Beyond ABC

Written by Lisa Holt & Lyn Wendon
Illustrated by Doreen Shaw

Based on characters originated by Lyn Wendon.

Welcome back to Letterland

As you may already know, the people and animals in Letterland usually hide behind their plain black letter shapes. Fortunately, in this book you can look into their secret land to see what they are really like. You will also discover some Letterland stories about what happens when these characters come together in words!

Are you ready?
Let's go!

Clever Cat belongs to Harry Hat Man. He looks after her well and she loves him. But she has one problem. As soon as she finds herself next to him in a word, she can't make her usual 'c...' sound because his hairy hat makes her nose tickle. So all you can hear when these two are together is Clever Cat's little sneezing sound, '**ch**...'.

Clever Cat was calmly playing **ch**ess in the kit**ch**en, but then the clock **ch**imed and Harry came hopping in to get his lun**ch**. He was horrified to see **ch**icks and a **ch**icken on a **ch**air, so he's been trying to **ch**ase them out. The trouble is, all that **ch**arging about has made Clever Cat start sneezing "**ch**" again! Let's help Harry **ch**oose his lun**ch** so he can hop off again. There's some **Ch**inese food, some **ch**eese and some **ch**unks of **ch**ocolate. There are some pea**ch**es and a **ch**erry cake, too. Whi**ch** would you **ch**oose for your lun**ch**?

chair   cheese   chicken   chocolate

ph

Harry Hat Man knows that Peter Puppy is sometimes sad because his ears droop. He also knows that Peter Puppy loves having his **ph**otogra**ph** taken. So whenever they sit together in a word Harry takes his **ph**otogra**ph**. Peter Puppy smiles and Harry Hat Man even laughs – quietly though – with his mouth half shut and his teeth on his lips. So his usual 'hhh...' sound becomes a 'fff...' sound, just like Firefighter Fred's sound. Hear it twice in the word **ph**otogra**ph**!

Today Harry is getting some tips from **Ph**illipa, the **ph**otogra**ph**er. She has won tro**ph**ies for her **ph**otos of dol**ph**ins and ele**ph**ants. Can you see them on the wall and on the pam**ph**lets? Look! She's **ph**otogra**ph**ing some **ph**easants. Harry took a **ph**oto of a saxo**ph**one and a sap**ph**ire this morning. Now he's taking another **ph**otogra**ph** of Peter Puppy to make him even happier.

dolphin   elephant   phone   photograph

sh

What sound does Sammy usually make in words? Yes, he likes to hiss 'sss…' very loudly. How does Harry Hat Man feel about noise? That's right, he hates it! So what do you think happens when Sammy comes slithering and sliding up behind Harry in a word? Do you think he will put up with all that noise? Absolutely not! He turns back and says "**sh**!" to hu**sh** Sammy up.

Sammy came slithering up behind Harry at the sea**sh**ore today, hissing loudly, so Harry had to say "**sh**!" again. Sammy and Harry like to sit in the sun**sh**ine and look at all the things by the **sh**ore. They can see **sh**ells, **sh**rimps and fi**sh** in the sea. Those fi**sh sh**ould keep a **sh**arp eye out for that **sh**ark in the **sh**allow water!

Can you see the **sh**epherd **sh**earing his **sh**eep? There are four **sh**y **sh**eep who don't want to be **sh**eared. Can you find them for him?

ship   shell   sheep   shark

When Tess and Harry get together in words you'll hear either the unvoiced **th** sound in **th**ink, or the voiced **th** sound, as in **there**.

Talking Tess spends a lot of time making her tiny 't…' sound in many words. But have you ever noticed **th**at Tess and Harry Hat Man make a completely different sound when **th**ey're toge**th**er? Talking Tess blames it on the wea**th**er – especially **th**understorms. Talking Tess loves **the th**understorms, but Harry hates **th**em – **th**ey're so loud! So Talking Tess hurries up to Harry to comfort him as she says, "**Th**ere, **th**ere. It's only **the th**under!"

Tess and Harry are hurrying home from **the th**eatre to get away from **the th**under. Nobody else seems bo**th**ered by **the th**under. **The th**rushes are **th**irsty so **th**ey are still in **th**eir bird ba**th**. **The** girl on **the th**rone hasn't put away her **th**imble and **th**read yet, and **the** a**th**lete by **the th**atched cottage is still **th**rowing his javelin. **Th**ankfully, I **th**ink **the th**under won't last more **th**an **th**irty seconds!

there   three   thirty   thunder   thumb

In a few words Harry gets so annoyed at Walter that he shouts, 'Who do you think you are?' and throws a bucket of water at Walter Walrus instead! Now who is too startled to speak? Yes, Walter Walrus!

Walter Walrus hates it **wh**en Harry Hat Man gets in his way so that he can't see ahead. Not only is Harry tall, but he also wears a hat, blocking Walter's view even more! So **wh**at does Walter do? He **wh**ooshes that hat off with a big wave of water! Then poor Harry Hat Man is too startled to speak. That is **wh**y we only hear Walter in words like **wh**en, **wh**ich, **wh**at, **wh**ere and **wh**y.

Look! Walter has **wh**acked Harry's hat off again, **wh**ile Harry wasn't looking! Perhaps Walter wants to see **wh**at the girl near the **wh**eeled bin is **wh**istling about. It looks like she has spotted a **wh**ale in the **wh**irlpool. The man with the **wh**ite shirt in the **wh**eat field hasn't seen the **wh**ale yet. Maybe he's just too busy **wh**ittling to notice it. **Wh**at do you think he might be **wh**ittling? Do you think his pet **wh**ippet hopes it will be something for him?

who   whale   wheat   wheel   white

Whenever you see Walter Walrus next to Annie Apple in a word, don't expect her to make her usual sound. That's because Walter Walrus is busy teasing her by splashing her with salty water. When he splashes Annie Apple we hear her cry out, "**AW**! Don't be so **aw**ful!"

It's d**aw**n in Letterland but Walter is already up to his tricks, splashing Annie on the l**aw**n while others are still y**aw**ning. Can you see the girl on the sees**aw** wearing a sh**aw**l? The little f**aw**n is watching her y**aw**n while the other f**aw**n is eating some str**aw**. Can you also see the sharp-beaked h**aw**k in the tree above the s**aw**? Do you think the h**aw**k feels like y**aw**ning too?

The cat is getting **aw**fully wet p**aw**s as she cr**aw**ls across the l**aw**n. How many p**aw** prints can you see on the l**aw**n?

dawn   lawn   paw   seesaw

ew

We know Walter Walrus is a trouble-maker. He loves to tease, and Eddy Elephant doesn't like being splashed. So when Eddy finds himself next to Walter Walrus in a word, he always acts first. He uses his trunk to squirt water at Walter instead. Walter is so surprised he cries out, "Oo! You!" That's why, when you see Eddy Elephant and Walter Walrus together in a word, you can be sure to hear an 'ew...'(oo) sound or a 'ew...'(you) sound.

Walter and Eddy are on the deck of a n**ew** ship. A cr**ew** member is busy handing out a f**ew** bags of cash**ew** nuts. There's a lovely vi**ew**, and there's a man intervi**ew**ing a fine lady in j**ew**els for the n**ew**s. The st**ew**ard is bringing them some delicious st**ew** served with n**ew** potatoes. You would think Walter and Eddy would be happy, but oh no, Eddy just bl**ew** some more water at Walter!

crew   jewels   news   view

Whenever you see Walter Walrus next to Oscar Orange in a word, guess what? You can expect trouble! Walter Walrus starts splashing salty water again and it gets in Oscar's eyes. But Walter always forgets that when you tease someone, you can end up hurting yourself too. Walter loses his balance and bumps his chin, so n**ow** they both h**ow**l, "**OW**!"

While Oscar and Walter are both h**ow**ling "**ow**!", the children are having fun chasing each other and playing with the inflatable v**ow**els d**ow**n in the pool. Not everyone is happy, though. Look at the lady fr**ow**ning as she holds up her dressing g**ow**n. Her g**ow**n and the t**ow**els are damp as they were too close to that p**ow**erful sh**ow**er. Can you see the cr**ow**d under the tree near the t**ow**er in the t**ow**n? Do you think they are looking at the c**ow**s? **H**ow many br**ow**n c**ow**s can you see?

brown   cow   owl   towel

No diving
allowed

Talcum
Powder

Mr O is an old man. He has been around for such a long time he kn**ow**s almost all there is to kn**ow**! So he kn**ow**s that Walter Walrus likes to tease Oscar Orange by splashing him. That's why whenever he can, he rushes up to protect Oscar in words, crying out, "**O**h no you don't!" In fact old Mr O cries "**O**h!" so loudly that Walter Walrus is too surprised to make any sound at all.

It's a lovely spring day in the mead**ow**. The sn**ow** has melted and the rabbits are busy building new burr**ow**s. A breeze is bl**ow**ing in the will**ow**s and hedger**ow**s. It's a perfect day for playing b**ow**ls and m**ow**ing the lawn. Mr O's cries have scared Walter, but he hasn't scared the cr**ow**s! Look, the farmer is s**ow**ing seeds and a cheeky cr**ow** is foll**ow**ing him. The farmer kn**ow**s that some of his seeds will still gr**ow**. He has already gr**ow**n some fine marr**ow**s for a sh**ow**. Can you see them in his wheel barr**ow**?

arrow   bungalow   window   yellow

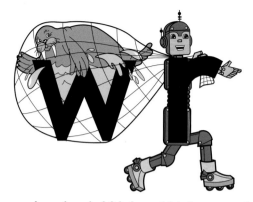

I expect you know that both Walter Walrus and Red Robot are trouble-makers in Letterland. So what happens when they meet? Well, Red Robot remembers that Walter causes trouble by splashing water around. But Red Robot doesn't want to get wet. So he quickly captures Walter Walrus in his sack. Then Walter is too shocked to speak! So whenever you see this troublesome pair in a word, expect to hear Red Robot growling 'rrr...' as he rolls along.

Red Robot has **wr**apped the sack around his **wr**ist so Walter can't **wr**iggle out. "What's **wr**ong with that?", Red Robot says to himself. The little **wr**ens are busy **wr**estling with **wr**iggling worms! Nobody has noticed the **wr**ecking ball knocking down the building behind. What a lot of rubbish in the **wr**eckage! There's some **wr**ought iron, a type**wr**iter, some **wr**apping paper and a poster for a **wr**estling match. **Wr**ite down what you can see in the **wr**eckage.

wrapper   wriggle   wrist   wrong

In Letterland, there are five rollerskating robots who cause trouble by capturing vowels even though they know they shouldn't. This one is called **Ar**thur **Ar** and he likes to capture Letterland apples. Look! He is running away with Annie Apple! She is too surprised to make her usual sound. Instead, all you can hear is **Ar**thur **Ar** reporting back to the ringleader, Red Robot, with his last name, "**Ar**!"

Arthur **Ar** waited until it was getting d**ar**k. He thought he could get up to his tricks by the light of the st**ar**s, but now he's stuck trying to escape from a l**ar**ge b**ar**n! The gu**ar**d dog has st**ar**ted b**ar**king to raise the al**ar**m. And now the f**ar**mer has found **Ar**thur's rad**ar** c**ar** p**ar**ked in his y**ar**d. **Ar**thur **Ar** is d**ar**ting around the b**ar**n trying to escape, but there's a guit**ar**, and t**ar**ts, sh**ar**p d**ar**ts and j**ar**s of v**ar**nish in his way. Even a little **ar**madillo is trying h**ar**d to catch **Ar**thur **Ar** and stop him from getting away in his rad**ar** c**ar**!

car farmer garden star

Now you need to learn about **Or**vil **Or**. He's another robot in Letterland who causes trouble by capturing vowels! **Or**vil **Or** likes to run away with oranges. When he is around, don't expect Oscar Orange to make his usual sound. All you can hear is **Or**vil **Or** rep**or**ting back to Red Robot with just one word, his last name, "**Or**!", as he rushes away to his boat by the sh**ore**.

Can you see **Or**vil's boat by the sh**ore**? It looks very st**or**my over there, doesn't it? There's an en**or**mous t**or**nado coming. It's heading for the **or**chard so unf**or**tunately the children playing sp**or**ts will have to run ind**oor**s. The st**or**m hasn't stopped **Or**vil **Or** though. As he f**or**ces his way past the h**or**se, it gives a little sn**or**t. But he had better not step on that little p**or**cupine. Can you see it, nibbling away on those ac**or**ns? How do you think **Or**vil will get past that cow with huge h**or**ns?

fork   horse   sport   storm

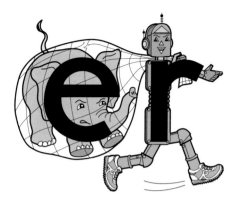

Now three of the five robots in Letterland are brothers: **Er**nest **Er**, Urgent Ur and Irving Ir. They all make the same sound as they report back to Red Robot, but they capture different vowels. First, let's meet **Er**nest **Er**, the robot who runs away with elephants! When you see **Er**nest **Er** in a word, don't expect to hear Eddy Elephant making his usual sound. All you can hear is **Er**nest **Er** calling out his last name, "**Er**!", as he reports back to Red Robot.

Ernest **Er** is a fast**er** runn**er** than his oth**er** robot broth**ers**. The park rang**er** is c**er**tain he won't be able to catch him as he runs past the bea**ver** and the p**er**ch and the ott**er** in the wat**er**. P**er**haps he will al**er**t the helicopt**er** to track down **Er**nest **Er** lat**er**. Right now, the rang**er** had bett**er** look aft**er** the badg**er** and the anteat**er** and the flow**er**s and f**er**ns. What oth**er** animals can you see? And who else can you see working in the park?

danger   flower   panther   tiger

This is **Ur**gent **Ur**. You won't see him very often, but when you do he'll be capturing umbrellas. He reports back to Red Robot with just one word, his last name, "**Ur**!" so you can't hear Uppy Umbrella making her usual sound. **Ur**gent **Ur** must have cold feet, because he always **tur**ns up wearing boots made of thick **cur**ly **pur**ple **fur**. The boots make him a slower runner than his other brothers so you hardly ever see him at the end of words.

What an eventful Th**ur**sday in Letterland! Everyone is talking about it! **Ur**gent **Ur** has jumped off the **cur**b and smashed an **ur**n. He is dist**ur**bing the **tur**keys too, though maybe now they'll **tur**n and see that fox l**ur**king in the bushes. There's a veterinary s**ur**geon's van near the girl who is b**ur**ning leaves. Do you think an animal has been h**ur**t? The cat **cur**led up by the **cur**tain doesn't seem to be h**ur**t. Maybe that n**ur**se will be needed to help the man in the h**ur**dle race. He's been h**ur**led right off his horse!

church   fur   nurse   purple

Irving **Ir** is the th**ir**d brother in the robot gang. He captures ink, then reports back to Red Robot with his last name, "**Ir**!" so you can't hear Impy Ink making his usual sound. **Ir**ving **Ir** gets into far fewer words than either of his brothers, because most of the ink bottles in Letterland make themselves invisible when they see **Ir**ving **Ir** coming. If Impy Ink gets caught he squ**ir**ts ink on to **Ir**ving's sh**ir**t! That's why v**ir**tually every sh**ir**t **Ir**ving owns is d**ir**ty!

Irving **Ir** has upset the g**ir**l behind him. She has been planning a th**ir**tieth b**ir**thday party for one of the clowns in the c**ir**cus. She has bought him a new sh**ir**t and cooked him some s**ir**loin steak and a b**ir**thday cake too! Now the clown with the hose really needs to squ**ir**t the ink off that brand new sh**ir**t! Do you think **Ir**ving **Ir** has seen the acrobats sw**ir**ling around and the g**ir**l tw**ir**ling her baton? Even the c**ir**cus dog is wh**ir**ling round in c**ir**cles.
Can you find th**ir**teen b**ir**ds here at the c**ir**cus today?

bird   dirt   shirt   skirt

There are five very important men in Letterland – the Vowel Men. You may have already met them. There is Mr A, the Apron Man and Mr E, the Easy Magic Man, Mr I, the Ice Cream Man, Mr O, the Old Man from over the ocean and Mr U, the Uniform Man. The five Vowel Men are the only Letterlanders that ever say their alphabet names in words – A! E! I! O! U!

But what happens when you see these Vowel Men out walking together in Letterland? Most of the time, all you need to do is remember this simple rhyme:

'When two Vowel Men go out walking, the first one does the talking.

The first one says his name, but his friend won't do the same.'

So in a word like **easy**, Mr E says his name "**E!**", while Mr A stays silent. That is because he is busy looking out for robots who cause trouble by capturing Vowel Men as they walk through Letterland.

Let's join some of the Vowel Men while they are out walking!

Mr A   Mr E   Mr I   Mr O   Mr U

When Mr A and Mr I go out walking, Mr A does the talking.
He just says his name, "**A**!", but his friend won't do the same. He's too busy being the lookout man, on guard against the robots!

Mr A and Mr I are out walking at the r**ai**lway station. They like to watch the tr**ai**ns. They even like w**ai**ting to see tr**ai**ns when it's r**ai**ning! It looks like some r**ai**n and h**ai**l are on the way. I'm afr**ai**d the man who is p**ai**nting the dr**ai**ns will compl**ai**n! But there's a beautiful r**ai**nbow and everyone else looks happy w**ai**ting for their tr**ai**n. There's a girl in a shiny r**ai**ncoat with a lovely d**ai**sy ch**ai**n, a boy m**ai**ling some letters, a s**ai**lor and his friend, and a man reading his d**ai**ly newspaper.

Do you think anyone will go on the Summer Tr**ai**l? They would ride on a tr**ai**n and then go s**ai**ling for a whole day!

paint   rain   sail   train

When Mr E and Mr A go out walking, Mr E usually does the talking. He just says his name, "**E**!", but his friend won't do the same. He's too busy looking out for robots!

Today Mr E and Mr A are out walking in the market. They **ea**ch have a list of things to buy to **ea**t. Can you find them some m**ea**t and some s**ea**food? They would also like h**ea**ps of fruit and vegetables. Can you find them some p**ea**ches, some b**ea**ns, and some p**ea**s? Mr E would like some t**ea** and some y**ea**st because he can't resist a ch**ea**p d**ea**l. He has also seen some expensive gl**ea**ming b**ea**ds, but luckily they are not within **ea**sy r**ea**ch! Mr A is pl**ea**sed as he has spotted a n**ea**t pile of j**ea**ns by that h**ea**p of l**ea**ves. And Mr E is b**ea**ming as he dr**ea**ms about the f**ea**st they will **ea**t when they get home. What a tr**ea**t!

jeans   peas   peaches   tea

When two Mr E's go out walking, the first Mr E does the talking. He just says his name, "**E**!", but his brother won't do the same. He's too busy looking out for robots!

Mr E and his brother are out for a quick walk. It's fr**ee**zing cold, so they n**ee**d to k**ee**p their f**ee**t moving. Behind them, a man is trying to sw**ee**p up the sl**ee**t and snow, but it is just too d**ee**p, and the br**ee**ze makes it difficult for him to s**ee**. It's so icy, the qu**ee**n is exc**ee**ding the sp**ee**d limit coming down the slippery, st**ee**p str**ee**t in her j**ee**p! She likes to come for coff**ee** m**ee**tings here once a w**ee**k. She's also often s**ee**n in the shops, sampling fine ch**ee**ses and buying sw**ee**ts. She loves toff**ee**, but she's never gr**ee**dy and afterwards she always brushes her t**ee**th.

The g**ee**se look happy f**ee**ding on s**ee**ds. They don't seem to mind having fr**ee**zing f**ee**t!

green   street   three   trees

When Mr O and his friend Mr A go out walking, Mr O does the talking. He just says his name, "**O**!", but his friend won't do the same. He's too busy looking out for robots!

Mr O and Mr A are out walking down by the **coa**st. They stopped at the fl**oa**ting B**oa**ters' Cafe to have a p**oa**ched egg on **toa**st. Everyone loves to eat p**oa**ched eggs and **toa**st there – even the g**oa**ts! They get b**oat** l**oa**ds of l**oa**ves delivered every day to make all the **toa**st they need! Can you see what is l**oa**ded in the b**oat** today?

Mr O and Mr A are walking towards the r**oa**d because they can see the Letterland c**oa**ch coming. They often like to travel by c**oa**ch on the r**oa**d along the c**oa**st with its beautiful views. Look out Mr A! Someone has left their socks s**oa**king in a bowl. Don't step on the s**oa**p and get s**oa**ked in the s**oa**py f**oa**m!

boat   coast   goat   toad

How to use this Letterland book

The *Letterland Beyond ABC* is designed for you to share actively with your children. As you read it, they will think of it all as simply fun. But with your help they will also be learning new vocabulary, many important letter combinations (digraphs) and vital listening, speaking and reading skills.

After each story, talk about the Letterland characters and the story reasons for their change of sound. Spend some time finding objects in the illustrations that contain the new sound. Let your listeners point to and speak out the word for each object, so they hear it repeatedly coming from their own mouths. Then re-read the story, all ears listening again for that recurring special sound.

Because every story combined with its illustration, clusters words of a kind, this book can also be a valuable memory aid for spelling. Seek out any missed objects in the lists below. They aren't all mentioned in the stories!

ch	kitchen	trophy	shield	Southport	wh	jigsaw	stew
chain	peaches		shingle	thank you card	whale	paw prints	steward
chair		**sh**	ship	thatched	wheat	saw	view
chalk	**ph**	bushes	shirt	theatre	wheateater	seesaw	yew tree
chart	alphabet cubes	dish	shoes	Thermos flask	wheeled bin	shawl	
checks	bibliography	fashion	shop	thick	wheel	strawberries	**ow**
cheese	digraphs	fish	shore	thimble	whelk	straws	brown
cherries	dolphin	mushroom	shorts	thin	whippet	trawler	down
chess	elephant	push	shrew	thirsty	whirl	yawn	clown
chest of drawers	graph	radish	shrimp	thirteenth	whirligig		cows
chicken	pamphlet	shades	shrub	thirtieth	whiskers	**ew**	crowd
chick peas	pharaoh	shadow	sunshine	thistle	whisky	cashew nuts	eyebrow
chicks	pheasant	shallow	washing	thorns	whistle	crew	flowers
chime	phone	shapes		thread	white	ewe	frown
chilli	phonics	shark	**th**	three	Whitley Bay	flew	gown
Chinese food	photographs	shed	athlete	throw	whittle	interview	howl
chocolate	photographer	sheep	bird bath	throne		jewels	shower
chop	physics	shear	birthday card	throat lozenge	**aw**	newspaper	talcum powder
chopsticks	sapphire	sheet	length	thrushes	coleslaw	new potatoes	town
chunks	saxophone	shell	month	thunder	dawn	preview	towel
chutney	sphere	shelves	mouthwash	toothbrush	fawn	screws	tower
hatch	xylophone	shepherd	path		hawk	shrew	trowel

46

owls
vowels

ow
arrow
blow
bungalow
bow
bowls
burrow
crow
flow
follow
glow
marrow
meadow
mow
narrow
rows
scarecrow
snow
sow
sparrow
swallow
tow
willows
wheel barrow
window
yellow

wr
typewriter
wrapping
wreath
wreck
wren
wrench

wrestling
wriggle
wrinkles
wring
wristwatch
writhe
writing paper
wrong
wrought iron

ar
archery board
alarm
armadillo
bark
barn
car
cart
carve/carving
chart
dark
dart
farmer
farmyard
garden
guitar
market
postcards
radar
scarlet scarf
star
tart
varnish

or
acorn
corn

corner
fork
horns
horse
morning
north
orchard
orchids
porcupine
sports
shore
score
stork
storm
shorts
tornado

er
anteater
badger
beaver
butterfly
carpenter
cleaner
danger
fern
flowers
hammer
helicopter
herbs
ladder
otter
painter
panther
perch
pliers
ranger

spider
tiger
timber
water
water lily
woodpecker

ur
burger
burn
burrs
conjurer
curb
curl
curtain
disturb
frankfurters
fur
furniture
hurdles
lurk
nurse
Saturday
surgery
Thursday
turkey
turnip
urn
windsurf

ir
birch
birds
birthday cake
circus
dirty
girder

girl
headfirst
fir cones
ladybird
shirt
sirloin steak
skirt
squirt
swirl
twirl

ai
chain
daisy chain
drain
grain
hail
mail
paid
painter
railway
rain
raisins
sail
sailor
snail
trail
train
waiter
waiting room

ea
beach
beads
beans
beat
cheap

cleaning
cream
deals
eagle
eat
jeans
leaves
lead
meat
neat
peaches
peak
peas
peat
seafood
seal
sea salt/shells
stream
tea
yeast

ee
asleep
bee
beef crisps
beetle
breeze
cheese
chimpanzee
coffee
feed
fleece
Fleet Street
freezing
geese
green
jeep

peel
queen
seed
sheet
sleep
speed
steep
steeple
sweep
sweets
three
toffee
trees

oa
boat
coach
coal
coast
coat
float
foal
foam
goal
goat
load
loaf
moat
oak
oats
poached
road
soak
soap
stoat
toad
toast

More from Letterland

The Letterland system teaches all 44 letter sounds in the English language through stories rather than rules. There are resources to take children from the very first stages of learning to full literacy. There are products for the classroom and many support products for use at home. Visit our website to see the full range, or contact your nearest supplier. A list of suppliers can be found on our website.

www.letterland.com

Letterland Living Code Cards allows you to display the cards on a white board or in your ICT suite.
- ✓ display each phoneme
- ✓ switch between font styles
- ✓ display plain or pictogram letters
- ✓ listen to the story behind the digraph
- ✓ watch the animated story
- ✓ listen to the phoneme
- ✓ view/listen to example words
- ✓ build words

The *Blends and Digraphs Songs* are a collection of 42 songs featuring the consonant blends and digraphs taught in the *Letterland Teacher's Guide*.

Letterland at school...

The *Letterland Teacher's Guide* introduces the alphabet with a Phonemic Awareness Fast Track and then goes on to cover the blends, digraphs, endings and silent magic **e**. It is clearly structured with lesson plans at the front and 32 pages of photocopiables, extension work and reinforcement at the back providing invaluable help with assessment. Special Child Strategies and Teacher Strategies accelerate learning while keeping it simple and fun.

The *Letterland Picture Code Cards* are a key resource for transferring Letterland learning to plain letters on the reverse sides. Features **a-z** and over 40 other phonemes and spelling patterns in the *Letterland Teacher's Guide*.
Plain letter sides include brief story explanations as well as useful example words.

Letterland at home...

The *Letterland ABC book* is a perfect introduction to all the **a-z** Letterland characters. If you haven't already got a copy of this book, then get one! It will prove a vital addition to your Letterland collection.

Letterland ABC Adventures software is specially designed for use at home. It introduces the **a-z** shapes and sounds in such a fun way that children don't even know they are learning!

There are plays, copymasters, posters, stickers, games, readers, DVDs, activity books, picture books and flashcards and more software. There is also an *Advanced* range of teaching materials focussing on more advanced blends and digraphs using Letterland stories too!

PV VENTURA/ HARPOON UNITS OF WORLD WAR 2

SERIES EDITOR: TONY HOLMES

OSPREY COMBAT AIRCRAFT • 34

PV VENTURA/ HARPOON UNITS OF WORLD WAR 2

Alan C Carey

OSPREY
PUBLISHING

Front Cover
Beginning in June 1944, US Navy PV-1 Venturas based in the Aleutian Islands of Alaska began harassing raids against Japanese military installations located in the northern Kurile Islands of Japan. Participating in one such mission against an enemy airfield on 21 July 1944 was Lt M A 'Butch' Mason, executive officer of VB-135. Approaching Shimushu, a mountainous island off Kamchatka Peninsula's southern coast, the Ventura's crew spotted eight Ki-44 'Tojo' fighters coming in to intercept them. As the fighters closed on the bomber, one peeled off and headed for the PV-1, but Mason instinctively flew his aircraft through a defensive 'split-S' manoeuvre and headed towards the airfield from whence the 'Tojos' had come. While tracers from the fighters flew past the Ventura's left side, and several bursts of anti-aircraft fire exploded behind, Mason instinctively opened the bomb-bay doors and 'pickled off' his bombs. Closing the doors, he dove the bomber down to the deck at 357 mph and headed for home.

Only one enemy fighter made an effort to pursue the PV-1, but top turret gunner Aviation Ordnance Mate 2nd Class (AOM2c) Richard McGee fired a burst from his twin 0.50-cal machine guns, which forced the Japanese pilot to break off the attack. The PV-1 (BuNo 48891) safely brought Mason and his crew back to their base on Attu Island. The aircraft depicted in this specially commissioned artwork survived many more missions before a crew from VPB-136 was forced to ditch it off Kodiak Island on 24 March 1945 (*Cover artwork by Iain Wyllie*)

Back cover
Ventura I AE774 of No 21 Sqn prepares to receive a mixed load of 250- and 500-lb bombs at Methwold in December 1942. This aircraft was badly shot up by German fighters over Holland on 3 February 1943, and although it managed to struggle back to Manston, in Kent, it was deemed to have been damaged beyond repair (*via Aeroplane*)

Title page spread
Venturas of the RNZAF's No 8 Sqn are readied for bombing up by No 10 Servicing Unit on Emirau Island on 14 February 1945 (*RNZAF Museum*)

First published in Great Britain in 2002 by Osprey Publishing, Midland House, West Way, Botley, Oxford OX2 0PH, UK
443 Park Avenue South, New York, NY 10016, USA

© 2002 Osprey Publishing Limited

ISBN 978 1 84176 383 5

Edited by Tony Holmes
Page design by Tony Truscott
Cover Artwork by Iain Wyllie
Aircraft Profiles by Tom Tullis
Scale Drawings by Mark Styling
Origination by Grasmere Digital Imaging, Leeds, UK
Printed and bound in China through Bookbuilders
Typeset in Adobe Garamond, Rockwell and Univers

08 09 10 11 12   11 10 9 8 7 6 5 4 3 2

ACKNOWLEDGEMENTS
Any errors in this work are the responsibility of the author. I would like to acknowledge the following Ventura veterans who assisted with this book: John Wallenburg (VB/VPB-130), 'Duke' Dillon (VB-133), Ward R Tifft (VB/VPB-133), Allen E Honeycutt (VPB-133), Ray Hurlbut (VPB-133), Perry A Litton (VPB-133), F T Pierce (VB-138), Ted Rowcliffe (VB-138), Doug Birdsall (VB-139), Will Swinney (VB/VPB-139), Ken Sanford (VB-140), Perry W Ustick Sr, (VB-148), Daryle Hahn (VPB-150), Elmer Olsen (VPB-151), Dick Kallage (VPB-153), 'Hutch' Hutchinson (VMF(N)-531), Wes Johnson (VMF(N)-531) and George Villasenor (FAW-4 Photographer).

I would also like to thank the following individuals and organisations: Tony Jarvis (Ventura Memorial Association Foundation), James Sawruk, Len Smallwood (VB/VPB-144 Association), Paul D Hosick (VMF(N)-531 Association), Bruce Robertson, Nick Stroud (*Aeroplane*), Hill Goodspeed (National Museum of Naval Aviation), Royal New Zealand Air Force Museum, Peter Devitt (Royal Air Force Museum, Hendon) and the National Archives and Records Administration (NARA).

EDITOR'S NOTE
To make this best-selling series as authoritative as possible, the Editor would be interested in hearing from any individual who may have relevant photographs, documentation or first-hand experiences relating to the world's combat aircraft, and the crews that flew them, in the various theatres of war. Any material used will be credited to its original source. Please write to Tony Holmes at 16 Sandilands, Chipstead, Sevenoaks, Kent, TN13 2SP, Great Britain, or by e-mail at: tony.holmes@zen.co.uk

CONTENTS

GENESIS

In 1939, the British Purchasing Commission requested that the Lockheed Aircraft Company provide it with a long-range anti-submarine patrol aircraft that boasted an adequate bomb load. Lockheed, which had built the A-29 Hudson bomber, proposed to the British an improved medium bomber based on the Model 18 Lodestar civilian transport.

The Model 37-21-01 resembled the Hudson but was heavier, and featured the more powerful Pratt & Whitney R-1850 S1A4-G Double Wasp air-cooled engine, which gave it a maximum speed of 312 mph (502 km/h). In addition, it had a range of 900 miles (1448 km), a bomb load of 2500 lbs (1134 kg) and a service ceiling of 25,000 ft (7620 m). In February 1940, the British placed an order for 25 aircraft, designated the Ventura I. Lockheed immediately sub-contracted the order to its subsidiary Vega in Burbank, California.

On 31 July 1941, the prototype Ventura I (AE658) flew for the first time. The aircraft was fitted with eight 0.303-in machine guns, two of which were mounted in a Boulton-Paul dorsal turret, two in the rear ventral fuselage and two fixed in the upper nose immediately ahead of the pilot. The final pair were also positioned in the nose on flexible mounts. As the RAF would later realise, the smaller calibre 0.303-in weapons would prove to be no match for cannon-armed German fighters such as the Bf 109 and Fw 190. The British Purchasing Board, impressed with the Ventura's performance, ordered an additional 650 aircraft. However, only 394 of these machines were actually delivered to Britain and her

Ventura I AE658 is seen aloft on its maiden flight, over southern California, on 31 July 1941. The aircraft's performance in early flights such as this one convinced the British to purchase the Lockheed bomber. AE658 was later posted to the Royal Canadian Air Force's No 34 Operational Training Unit (OTU) at Pennfield Ridge, New Brunswick, where it served from 29 July 1942 to 25 July 1943 as a trainer for bomber crews. On the latter date, the aircraft bounced on landing at Pennfield Ridge, swung out of control and suffered the collapse of one of its undercarriage legs. AE658 was subsequently declared a write-off and scrapped (*via Tony Holmes*)

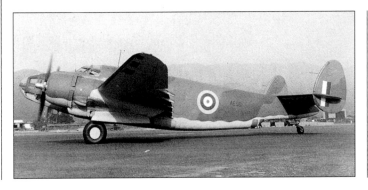

The subject of this official Lockheed photograph (Ventura I AE661) also went north to Canada in mid-1942 to serve with No 34 OTU at Pennfield Ridge. The bomber was written off just 19 days before AE658 when it suffered a burst tyre on take-off, which caused an uncontrolled swing that was only stopped by the pilot raising the undercarriage whilst the Ventura was still on the ground (*via Michael O'Leary*)

Commonwealth forces, as the US Navy requisitioned the remainder in the aftermath of the Pearl Harbor attack on 7 December 1941.

The aircraft evolved as requirements for it changed, with the Ventura II/IIA and GR V (the US equivalents were the PV-1 and PV-3) eventually entering operational service. Between December 1941 and May 1944, Lockheed-Vega built 2493 examples of the Ventura.

The Ventura II was similar to the first production model, except that it was powered by the military-rated Pratt & Whitney R-2800-31 engines and had a bomb-bay capable of carrying 3000 lbs (1360 kg) of ordnance. The Ventura IIA had its British turret and guns replaced with their American-made equivalents consisting of the Martin upper turret with two 0.50-cal machine guns, two fixed 0.50-cal and two flexible 0.30-cal guns in the nose, and another pair of 'thirties' in the ventral position.

Great Britain ordered 487 Mk IIs, although following Pearl Harbor most of these were taken over by the United States Army Air Force (USAAF) and used for training. In 1943, 43 of these aircraft were delivered to the Royal Australian Air Force (RAAF) and the Royal New Zealand Air Force (RNZAF).

The Mk II also operated with the designations B-34-VE, B-34A-3-VE, O-56, RB-34B, O-56-LO and finally B-37 during its service with the USAAF.

PV-1 VENTURA

By the spring of 1942, the US Navy had realised that its vast fleet of amphibious patrol aircraft (typified by the Consolidated PBY Catalina) were too slow and lightly armed to protect themselves from enemy aircraft. Therefore, the hasty procurement of aircraft began, with the

This photo of Ventura I AE748 flying over typically English countryside was taken in the late summer of 1942. Never issued to a frontline unit, the bomber initially served with the Aeroplane & Armament Experimental Establishment (A&AEE) at Boscombe Down, before being passed on to the Empire Central Flying School. It was finally struck off charge on 9 August 1945. Clearly visible is the Boulton-Paul turret fitted with two 0.303-in guns, which proved no match for German fighters. Few RAF crews liked the Ventura, yet it could take heavy battle damage and still return home (*via Bruce Robertson*)

An underside view of Ventura I AE748 (*via Bruce Robertson*)

Equipped with a Martin upper turret, this B-34 is seen patrolling the California coast in late 1942. The aircraft has become an impromptu target for an AT-6 that is no doubt being flown by a tyro fighter pilot under training. In a repeat of this scene halfway across the globe in western Europe, RAF crews were at the same time facing far deadlier foes flying Fw 190s and Bf 109s (*via Bruce Robertson*)

service obtaining a quantity of surplus B-34 Venturas and B-24 Liberators from USAAF stocks.

The decision to outfit Navy squadrons with Venturas was based primarily on two characteristics of the aircraft – its speed and armament. The PV-1 (the Navy designation meaning Patrol Vega) was similar to the Ventura B-34/Mk IIA except for the installation of the ASD-1 search radar (Mk IV radar was installed in the US Marine Corps nightfighter variant), navigational instruments and additional fuel tanks, which

Adorned with a falling bomb and the legend *JAPPY LANDINGS* on the crew entry door aft of the 'star and bar', this weary B-34 still wears its RAF serial (FD719), painted in black, beneath the tail section (*via Bruce Robertson*)

Tasked with the vital role of protecting allied convoys sailing from the United States to Europe, the US Navy's PV-1 squadrons flew countless sorties along the Atlantic coast of America. Seen on a pre-delivery flight, this aircraft is painted in the standard Navy Measure II ASW colour scheme. This high-visibility camouflage was used only in areas where enemy aircraft would not be encountered (*via the Author*)

The cockpit of a Ventura GR V of the RCAF's No 1 Air Armament Squadron, based at Trenton, Ontario. This late model machine had dual controls, whereas earlier Ventura variants (including those used by the US Navy) were equipped with controls for one pilot only. The Vega factory subsequently produced a kit that allowed older aircraft to be modified to this configuration 'in the field' (*Ken Goodall via VMAF*)

extended the aircraft's range to 1660 miles (2670 km).

Early versions of the PV-1 carried two fixed 0.50-cal guns installed in the nose, two in the Martin upper turret and two 0.30-cal guns in the ventral position. Later models had three 0.50-cal guns in a chin package under the nose, which replaced the bombardier station, as well as rocket launchers installed beneath each wing.

The maiden flight of the PV-1 took place on 3 November 1942, and approximately 1600 aircraft were produced between December 1942 and May 1944. All US Navy aircraft featured a Bureau of Aeronautics (BuNo) number, with PV-1s being assigned BuNos 29723 to 29922, 34586 to 34997, 33067 to 33466, 48652 to 48939 and 49360 to 49659. The British acquired 387 aircraft of a similar configuration, designating them as the General Reconnaissance (GR) Mk V.

PV-2 HARPOON

Soon after the PV-1 entered service, Lockheed began designing a new

Graceful in flight, a standard production US Navy PV-1 Ventura cruises off the California coast on a pre-delivery acceptance flight in early 1944 (*Lockheed via Michael O'Leary*)

Near-identically camouflaged to the PV-1 seen at the bottom of the previous page, this PV-2 Harpoon was officially photographed by Lockheed overflying a snowy Californian landscape in early 1945 (*via Michael O'Leary*)

aircraft that would better fit the needs of the US Navy. The result was the Vega Model 15, which was duly designated the PV-2 Harpoon in naval service. The prototype was flown in November 1943, and full production began at Vega's Burbank plant in March 1944.

The PV-2 had an entirely redesigned tail assembly, which improved single-engine performance, and a wingspan of 75 ft (23 m). Armament consisted of two fixed 0.50-cal machine guns in the nose, three fixed 0.50-cal guns in the chin package and the PV-1's 0.50-cal-equipped top turret and ventral position. The Harpoon's internal bomb load capacity was increased to 4000 lbs (1814 kg). Although the new patrol bomber retained the PV-1's Pratt & Whitney R-2800-31 engines, the aeroplane had reduced climbing speed and a top speed of 282 mph (453 km/h) due to its increased all up weight. Finally, the addition of extra fuel tanks boosted the PV-2's range to 1790 miles (2880 km), compared with the PV-1's 1660 miles (2670 km). These new integral wing tanks proved difficult to seal, and the PV-2's operational debut was delayed as a result. The first 30 Harpoons were delivered with the faulty seals, and these aircraft were designated as PV-2Cs and used exclusively for training. Hence, by the end of 1944, Lockheed only delivered 69 aircraft.

This early production PV-2 was decorated with the new variant's menacing name for a series of Lockheed publicity photos taken in the vicinity of Los Angeles in early 1944 (*via Bruce Robertson*)

An additional problem with wing spars caused squadrons operating Harpoons to ground the aircraft between April and May 1945.

A later model Harpoon, designated the PV-2D, had eight fixed 0.50-cal guns in the nose, and 35 of these were delivered to the Navy before the end of World War 2. Some were also diverted to the Portuguese Air Force. By September 1945, Lockheed-Vega had manufactured 535 Harpoons.

The PV-2's extended wingspan and trio of 0.50-cal guns in the nose are clearly visible in this underside view (*via Bruce Robertson*)

VENTURA SQUADRONS OF THE RAF

The first two Ventura Is (AE662 and AE680) destined for service with the RAF reached Britain aboard the merchant ship SS *Ocean Voyager* on 10 April 1942, with an additional ten arriving ten days later. The aircraft were assembled, test flown and sent to Bomber Command's No 2 Group. However, by the time the Venturas arrived in the frontline, the aircraft's role had, crucially, been changed from anti-submarine warfare to daylight bombing. Now, the principal missions flown by the aircraft would be short-range night operations against heavily defended targets on land, and the low-level support of the Army in the field. It would fail to meet the RAF's expectations in either role.

The Air Force needed a fast, low-level bomber to replace the obsolescent, and vulnerable, Bristol Blenheim, and the unavailability of any other aircraft (the A-20 Douglas Boston had been considered, but there were too few in the UK at the time) necessitated the use of the Ventura.

No 21 Sqn

In late April 1942, a training group arrived at Bodney, in Norfolk, to oversee No 21 Sqn's conversion from the Blenheim IV to the Ventura. On 31 May, the unit accepted AE685 and AE681, and familiarisation with the aircraft began. During training, various problems were encountered such as leaky fuel tanks, vacuum pumps that seized and faulty navigation equipment. It did not take long for the crews to nickname the Ventura the 'pig', stating that it was both less manoeuvrable and slower than the

Ventura I AE794 was one of the first Lockheed bombers delivered to No 21 Sqn in the summer of 1942. It was eventually written off when its undercarriage collapsed in a heavy landing at Methwold on 26 January 1943 (*via VMAF*)

Mosquito, which was then entering service with No 2 Group. To cap it all off, the Lockheed bomber's controls were sluggish.

From the outset, the Ventura was not well received by the men that took them into battle, and some wondered why they had been selected to fly it. Their dislike of the aircraft's performance was summed up in a popular joke amongst RAF aircrew at the time. 'What can the Ventura do that the Hudson can't? Drink more petrol!'

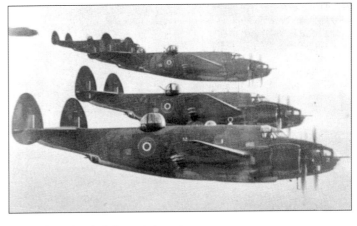

By August 1942, No 21 Sqn was up to strength, and nightflying training began under the leadership of the squadron commander, Wg Cdr Pritchard. The following month night intruder training commenced over Mildenhall, and on 31 October the unit transferred to nearby Methwold. Three days later No 21 Sqn undertook it first operation when three Venturas attacked railway marshalling yards at Hengelo, in Holland.

In misty conditions, Wg Cdr Pritchard led the attack and bombed a railway line, while Flt Lt Dennis struck an identical target between Apeldoorn and Amersfoort, again in Holland. The third aircraft, however, did not drop its bombs, crash-landing instead at Tollesbury, on the Essex coast. Another attack followed three days later, with two separate strikes taking place against German shipping along the Dutch coast. The first group, led by Wg Cdr Werfield, failed to locate the intended shipping at Maassluis, and instead bombed another vessel in the port of Rotterdam. One aircraft failed to return from the mission.

The following day, Venturas were sent out again in a low-level attack against various targets around Gent and Terneuzen, on the Belgian–Dutch border. Flt Sgt Hoggarty bombed an airfield and Sqn Ldr Ray Chance attacked a ship in the Scheldt Estuary. However, WO V R Henry's AE734 was hit by flak and crashed in the sea off Vlissingen.

On 23 December, six Venturas attacked the torpedo workshops and naval barracks at Den Helder. This mission was deemed a success, as 36 of the 42 bombs dropped hit the target, halting work for a month.

Above and below
These two photographs of a flight of Ventura IIs of No 21 Sqn were taken on 12 January 1943 when the bomber was officially introduced to the British Press. The aircraft closest to the camera in the top shot (and in the the centre of the leading section below) is AE856, which was flown by squadron CO Wg Cdr R J P Pritchard on the Philips raid on 6 December 1942. This aircraft later served with No 1407 Meteorological Flight, based in Reykjavik, Iceland. AE856 was written off on 22 April 1944 when it crashed soon after taking off from the Icelandic capital *(F R Lucas via VMAF (above) and via Tony Holmes (below))*

Mission photographs of a raid on the docks at Den Helder, in the Netherlands, by six No 21 Sqn Venturas on 23 December 1942. This mission took place 17 days after the attack on the Philips factory at Eindhoven in which nine Venturas from Nos 21, 464 and 487 Sqns were lost (*F R Lucas via VMAF*)

Barracks, buildings and three cranes were also damaged, and a ferry and tugboat sunk.

Nos 464 and 487 Sqns

While 21 Sqn tested the new bomber against targets in Holland, two additional Ventura units were formed at Feltwell, in Norfolk – Australian-manned No 464 Sqn, led by Wg Cdr R H Young, and New Zealand-manned No 487 Sqn, led by Wg Cdr F C Seavill. Both established on 15 August 1942, the units practised low-level flying in preparation for a raid against the Philips radio and valve factory at Eindhoven, in Holland, that was scheduled for December. This mission strike would be the first real test for the Ventura.

The factory, located in a heavily populated area of the Dutch city, was the largest producer of valves in Europe, and provided about one-third of Germany's supply of valves and radar equipment. The attack, code-named Operation *Oyster*, would be No 2 Group's most ambitious raid of the war to date, with all three Ventura squadrons participating, along with Boston IIIs of Nos 88, 107 and 226 Sqns and Mosquito B IVs of Nos 105 and 139 Sqns.

The attacking force was split in two, with Nos 464 and 487 Sqns taking part in the attack on the Stryp Group plant, along with Nos 105, 107 and 139 Sqns. No 21 Sqn would hit the Emmasingel valve factory, as would Nos 88 and 226 Sqns. The Boston and Mosquito units would precede the Venturas to the target by six minutes.

Ventura II AE839 served exclusively with No 21 Sqn, and it is seen here between missions at Methwold in January 1943. This machine was hit by both flak and fighters whilst attacking a tanker in Brest harbour on 5 April. One of three aircraft lost by the squadron on this date, AE839 was ditched just off the French coast (*via Bruce Robertson*)

With most of its port stabilator missing, cannon holes in the wing and a collapsed tail oleo, this anonymous No 464 Sqn Ventura II makes for a sorry sight at Methwold in the spring of 1943. Lucky to have made it back to base, a grim-faced Flg Off Parsons contemplates what might have been had that 20 mm shell hole in the left wing been two of three feet further forward (*via Bruce Robertson*)

At 1120 hrs on 6 December, Wg Cdr R H Young of No 464 Sqn led 47 Venturas (each loaded with 250-lb delayed action bombs and 30-lb incendiaries) on the raid. There were mixed feelings among the participating crews, who wished they were flying the faster Mosquito or Boston.

The weather was clear as the formations headed over the North Sea and the Dutch coast. Once the Venturas reached occupied territory, flying at a height of just 200 ft (60 m), they immediately came under intense anti-aircraft fire as they crossed Woensdrecht airfield. The first formation to overfly the base lost Ventura II AJ213 of No 464 Sqn (flown by Sgt S C Moss) to flak, and had another two bombers damaged. Moments later, the leading Ventura of the second formation (AJ196, flown by Wg Cdr Seavill) was also struck by flak and hit the ground, exploding on impact. A second No 487 Sqn machine, flown by Sqn Ldr Carlisle, was hit in the starboard engine by a 20 mm shell, while the No 464 Sqn aircraft of Sgt Smock had five feet shot off one wing. Seconds later the surviving Venturas were clear of the airfield and heading for Eindhoven.

As they approached the targets, smoke from the first two waves obscured the factory and made bombing difficult. Intense flak from gun positions on, and near, buildings greeted the Venturas, and several more aircraft were shot down, or crashed into houses. No 464 Sqn's AE702 (flown by Flg Off H G Moore) and AE945 (flown by Sgt B M Harvey RCAF) were lost, while No 487 Sqn flight commander Sqn Ldr Leonard H Trent saw one of his unit's Venturas (AE902) explode near his own aircraft. The remaining crews dropped their bombs and headed home.

The trip back was uneventful, except that AE697 of No 21 Sqn was forced to ditch, although the crew was rescued. In all, nine Venturas were lost and 27 were damaged in the attack (many of the latter by a large gaggle of low-flying ducks encountered en route to the target!). Only one bomber made it back to base unscathed. Losses were evenly split among the squadrons, with each losing three machines, but the factory sustained considerable damage and was put out of action for several days. However, the loss of nine aircraft did not help establish faith in the Ventura.

CIRCUS OPERATIONS

After Eindhoven, the squadrons changed tactics and began flying medium altitude missions against railway marshalling yards, factories, and airfields in northern France, Holland and Belgium. Codenamed Circus, these operations were strongly escorted by fighters, being designed to draw enemy fighters into combat. And although the bomber units continued to meet heavy opposition from enemy fighters and flak during Circus missions, losses proved to be much lighter.

The first Circus involving the Ventura was flown on 9 January 1943 against the Royal Dutch Steel Works at Ijmuiden. Wg Cdr Pritchard led 12 Venturas that bombed from 8000 ft (2438 m), damaging coking ovens, a benzole plant and other buildings. Four days later, Fw 190 dispersal areas at Abbeville/Drucat became the targets for 18 Venturas of Nos 21 and 464 Sqns. During the attack, German fighters came up to intercept, but they were successfully driven off by escorting Spitfires.

A combined mission involving 18 aircraft from Nos 21, 464 and 487 Sqns took place on the 22 January against dispersal areas at Cherbourg/Maupertuis airfield. As Wg Cdr Pritchard led the formation over the English Channel, a No 464 Sqn Ventura piloted by Sgt Powell unexpectedly plunged into the water. Things got no any better as the formation arrived over the target at 9000 ft (2743 m), for they were greeted by intense flak. No 487 Sqn's Flg Off Perryman felt his aircraft take hits, and he was forced to ditch 20 miles (32 km) off the Isle of Wight.

Circus operations continued into February, with 12 aircraft from No 21 Sqn, led by Wg Cdr King, hitting the airfield at Courtrai/Wevelghen on the 3rd. This time, they were met by both intense flak and enemy fighters, with the Fw 190s attacking from head-on. Sgt K G Moodey's aircraft was shot down and two more Venturas were seriously damaged at the cost of one German fighter claimed by King's turret gunner.

Enemy flak and fighters continued to interfere with Ventura operations. On 10 February No 487 Sqn bombed marshalling yards at Caen, and its escorting Spitfire VBs of No 485 Sqn were jumped by Fw 190s and four fighters lost. On the 26th, No 464 Sqn found out at first- hand the accuracy of German flak gunners when every Ventura was damaged during an attack on shipping at Dunkirk. Nearing the target area, Sqn Ldr Dale and his navigator were blinded when a shell shattered the windscreen of AE847 and he had to crash-land his aeroplane back at base – it was later repaired and returned to service. The following day, the Ventura units were pulled from action to participate in Exercise *Spartan* (the most important tactical exercise held in the UK during the war, which tested plans being made for the eventual invasion of France), and they would not return to Circus operations until 28 March.

BACK IN ACTION

On 28 March, 24 Venturas from Nos 464 and 487 Sqns went back to conducting attacks against shipping dock areas around Rotterdam. Six ships were damaged, including a 470-ft vessel, and shipyards

A ten-mission veteran, this No 487 Sqn Ventura II is being loaded up with incendiary bomb cannisters by the hard-working groundcrews at Methwold in April 1943 (*Larry Milberry via VMAF*)

Canadian navigator Plt Off Jack Fleming (on the right) converses with his crew in front of their personalised No 464 Sqn Ventura II *Joybelle* at Methwold in the spring of 1943. This aircraft boasts 18 mission markings, nose art and 'teeth' on the bomb aimer's Perspex window framing. A typical Ventura crew consisted of four to five men. A considerable number of Canadians served with all three Ventura units in 1942–43 (*Pam Fleming via VMAF*)

Three 250-lb bombs are carefully wheeled into position on their trolley beneath the open bomb-bay of a Ventura 'somewhere in England' in 1943 (*Comox Air Force Museum via VMAF*)

were bombed. All aircraft returned home safely, and three strikes were scheduled for the next day. The following morning (0900 hrs) Wg Cdr King returned to Rotterdam with 24 aircraft, but this time the raids were not as successful for a heavy overcast obscured the target, causing No 21 Sqn to bomb barges at Dordrecht instead. Nos 464 and 487 Sqns bombed nearby railroad installations, where they were opposed by heavy flak that damaged seven aircraft.

At noon, 24 more Venturas under the command of Wg Cdr Sugden attempted to bomb marshalling yards at Abbeville, but strong winds caused the ordnance to miss the target. Later in the day, Rotterdam was visited once again by a force of 24 Venturas.

In early April, Nos 464 and 487 Sqns were transferred to Methwold, while No 21 Sqn moved north to Oulton. Operations resumed on 4 April, with the squadrons returning to Rotterdam. The Venturas met heavy flak and 20 aircraft were damaged, including one flown by No 464 Sqn's Sgt Lush, which fell behind and was eventually shot down by Fw 190s. Meanwhile, Flt Lt Dennis of No 21 Sqn had led aircraft from his unit on a cloudless day against an oil tanker discovered in the French port of Brest. The ship was already seriously damaged and well ablaze by the time the Venturas were bounced by 15 Fw 190s. Despite the protection of escorting Spitfires from the Ibsley Wing's Nos 65 and 602 Sqns, two Venturas were shot down and two more so badly damaged that their crews were forced to ditch during the flight home.

On 13 April Fw 190s intercepted 11 Venturas from No 487 Sqn near Caen. However, the escorting Spitfires from Nos 331 and 332 Sqns intercepted the Fw 190s, which were swiftly driven off. Eight days later 11 aircraft from No 21 Sqn, led by Flt Lt Dennis, hit marshalling yards at Abbeville, and defending Fw 190s succeeded in flying through the protecting escorts and shooting down three Venturas.

During the month of April, the trio of Ventura squadrons had flown 18 Circus operations, consisting of 254 sorties.

On 2 May No 464 Sqn bombed the Royal Dutch Steel Works at Ijmuiden once again, causing considerable damage to factory buildings and sinking two ships, although the steel works were not hit. Soon after leaving the target they were intercepted by Fw 190s, which damaged two aircraft and wounded a crewman.

RAMROD 16

On 3 May Boston IIIA-equipped No 107 Sqn attacked the Royal Dutch Steel Works at low level, while No 487 Sqn flew a diversionary raid against a power station in Amsterdam. Designated Ramrod 16, this mission would prove disastrous for the New Zealanders.

The crews had been told to expect heavy opposition, but that they had to press home their attacks as a means of encouraging Dutch resistance fighters on the ground. Unbeknown to the attacking forces, a group of Luftwaffe fighters had been placed on alert to cover the arrival of the German governor of Holland to the nearby town of Haarlem. To make matters worse, a squadron of escorting Spitfires from No 11 Group had arrived at the rendezvous point 30 minutes too soon, placing the Germans on high alert. Fw 190s of II./JG 1 flew to intercept the British fighters, while Bf 109s of 2./JG 27 tackled the unsuspecting bombers.

The Venturas flew in two formations, led by Sqn Ldr Leonard Trent in AJ209 and Flt Lt A V Duffill in AE916. Near the Dutch coast, the two sections climbed to 12,000 ft (3657 m), whereupon a force of 70 German fighters attacked them. Duffill's aircraft quickly became the target of a Bf 109, which shot away his hydraulic system, set both engines ablaze and wounded two crew members. The pilot managed to keep the bomber in the air and eventually land safely back at Methwold. His would be the only Ventura to make it back to England.

As Flt Lt Duffill fought to save his aircraft, two more Venturas in his section were shot down. Sqn Ldr Trent struck back when he fired a short burst from his nose guns at an enemy fighter that flew past him.

His transmissions log open on his desk, an anonymous wireless operator took this snap of his 'office' during a mission over France in 1943 (*Joe Ouelett via Larry Milberry/VMAF*)

King George VI and Queen Elizabeth visited No 487 Sqn at Methwold on 26 May 1943 to pass on their condolences to the surviving members of the unit three weeks after the disastrous 3 May Amsterdam power station raid. Having lost 11 of the 12 Venturas sortied that day, the unit was declared non-operational for two weeks while replacement aircraft and crews were swiftly posted in (*John Robinson via VMAF*)

The fighter went down in flames. As the survivors headed for the target, there were only three Venturas left. Nearing the power station, another bomber was shot down, followed by another. Trent was now alone.

During the aerial battle, there were instances of bravery and luck among the Ventura crews. In the minutes prior to their bomber (AE780) being shot down, resulting in their death, Flg Offs McGowan and Thornber had placed a parachute on their wounded gunner and pushed him out of the striken Ventura – he was the only survivor from the crew. Flg Off Coshall's aircraft (AE684) had been blown apart, killing him instantly, but Sgt Stannard had had a miraculous escape when the severed tail section of the bomber, which he was occupying, glided safely down to the ground and he was taken prisoner.

Nearing the target, Sqn Ldr Trent released his bombs just as the Ventura was hit at 7000 ft (2133 m), and he and his navigator were thrown clear at this height and descended by parachute into captivity. The rest of the crew did not escape the shattered Ventura.

The Amsterdam raid claimed 11 of the 12 Venturas sortied, and caused the RAF to question the suitability of the aircraft to daytime bombing missions. Three days later No 487 Sqn could muster only six crews and eight aircraft. Sqn Ldr A G Wilson arrived soon afterwards and began rebuilding the unit. On 26 May, King George VI arrived to pay his respects to the squadron that had been obliterated three weeks earlier. By the end of the month No 487 Sqn was back in business.

As a postscript to this mission, on 1 March 1946 Sqn Ldr Leonard Trent was awarded a Victoria Cross for his outstanding leadership of 'B Flight' on this raid. Indeed, his exploits only became known after he was repatriated following two years in a PoW camp. The citation accompanying Trent's award of Britain's highest military honour read as follows:

'On the 3rd May 1943, Sqn Ldr Trent was detailed to lead a formation of Ventura aircraft in a daylight attack on the power station at Amsterdam. This operation was intended to encourage Dutch workmen in their resistance to enemy pressure. The target was known to be heavily defended. The importance of bombing it, regardless of enemy fighters or anti-aircraft fire, was strongly impressed on the aircrews taking part in the operation. Before taking off, Sqn Ldr Trent told the deputy leader that he was going over the target, whatever happened.

'All went well until the 11 Venturas and their fighter escort were nearing the Dutch coast. Then one bomber was hit and had to turn back. Suddenly large numbers of enemy fighters appeared. Our escorting fighters were hotly engaged and lost touch with the bombing force. The Venturas closed up for mutual protection and commenced their run up to the target. Unfortunately, the fighters detailed to support them over the target had reached the area too early and had been recalled.

'Soon the bombers were attacked. They were at the mercy of 15 to 20 Messerschmitts, which dived on them incessantly. Within four minutes six Venturas were destroyed. Sqn Ldr Trent continued on his course with the three remaining aircraft.

'In a short time two more Venturas went down in flames. Heedless of the murderous attacks, and of the heavy anti-aircraft fire which was now encountered, Sqn Ldr Trent completed an accurate bombing run and even shot down a Messerschmitt at point-blank range. Dropping his bombs in the target area, he turned away. The aircraft following him was shot down on reaching the target. Immediately afterwards his own aircraft was hit, went into a spin and broke up. Sqn Ldr Trent and his navigator were thrown clear and became prisoners of war. The other two members of the crew perished.

'On this, his 24th sortie, Sqn Ldr Trent showed outstanding leadership. Such was the trust placed in this gallant officer that the other pilots followed him unwaveringly. His cool, unflinching courage and devotion to duty in the face of overwhelming odds rank with the finest examples of these virtues.'

FINALE

In June 1943, No 2 Group left Bomber Command and joined the 2nd Tactical Air Force. Strikes continued as heavy flak and German fighters continued to take a toll on the trio of Ventura units. For No 487 Sqn, operations were again suspended for a few days after a raid on Caen when Ventura AE797 was shot down. On the 13th, No 464 Sqn was ordered to attack St Brieue viaduct. Nearing the coast, they were bounced by Fw 190s, which shot down Flt Sgt Kane-Maguire in AE937 and damaged two more aircraft.

On 24 June, No 487 Sqn flew its last Ventura mission against Mauperthuis airfield, near Paris. The following month the unit moved to Sculthorpe, again in Norfolk, and commenced re-equipment with Mosquito FB VIs. No 464 Sqn followed suit on 21 July,

A typical four-man crew from No 464 Sqn pose for the camera at Feltwell in early 1943. They are, from left to right, Sgts Cec McKennon RAF, Bert Orress RAF, Ted Elton RAAF and Keith MacIntosh RCAF *(Keith MacIntosh via VMAF)*

Ventura II AJ206 served exclusively as a trials aircraft during its career with the RAF. Here, the bomber has been fitted with 5-in High Velocity Aerial Rockets beneath its port wing (*via Bruce Robertson*)

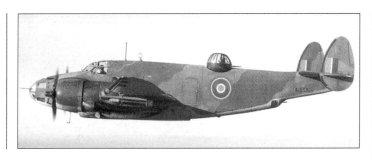

Personnel of No 500 'County of Kent' Sqn pose for an official group photograph just weeks after converting from the Hudson V to the Ventura II at La Senia, in Algeria (*Al Edwards via VMAF*)

This photograph was taken from an RAF Ventura flying a convoy patrol over the North Atlantic after the 2nd Tactical Air Force had replaced the last of its Venturas with Mosquitoes and Boston IIIs in September 1943 (*Mike Dzick via VMAF*)

leaving only No 21 Sqn with the Ventura II. In August the final Ventura squadron participated in three bombing missions before moving to Hartford Bridge, in Hampshire, to participate in Operation *Starkey*.

The operation's purpose was to make the Germans believe that an invasion was near, thus drawing the Luftwaffe into a major air battle and forcing them to bring back large forces from Italy. As part of the ruse heavy raids were directed against German military targets, and on 8 September No 21 Sqn bombed the marshalling yards at Abbeville without suffering any losses. The following day the unit carried out its last Ventura missions with two raids against gun positions at Boulogne and Merville airfield. By October the unit was operating Mosquito FB VIs from Sculthorpe.

SUPPLEMENTARY RAF VENTURA OPERATIONS

Between November 1942 and September 1943, Nos 21, 464 and 487 Sqns flew 1251 sorties for the loss of 30–35 aircraft. Although removed from No 2 Group, Venturas continued to fly with the RAF in a reduced capacity as maritime reconnaissance aircraft in the Mediterranean. In October 1943, No 13 Sqn, operating as part of the Northwest African Coastal Air Force, converted to Ventura GR Vs at Sidi Amor, in Tunisia, but was quickly re-equipped with Martin Baltimore IVs in January 1944. No 500 'County of Kent' Sqn replaced its Hudsons with Ventura GR Vs in

December 1943 at La Senia, in Algeria, and used them for anti-submarine patrols over the western Mediterranean during1944.It also set up detachments at several other airfields in the region to support anti-shipping operations north of Corsica.

The highlight of this period occurred on 19 May 1944, when American destroyers spotted the U-960 in the Mediterranean north-west of Algiers. The submarine was forced to surface, and a No 500 Sqn Ventura, piloted by Flt Off Mundy, bombed it with depth charges. The submarine sank, taking 31 of its 51-man crew with it. The unit replaced it's Venturas with Baltimore IV/Vs in the autumn of 1944.

The RAF continued using Venturas until war's end, the GR V variant performing both unglamorous meteorological flights and clandestine missions with Nos 251, 299, 519, 521 and 624 Sqns. No 521 Sqn was equipped with the aircraft from late 1943 through to October 1944, with its operational sectors covering the North Sea and North Atlantic. No 624 Sqn briefly used Ventura IIs during the autumn of 1943 to drop

Ventura GR V FN966 served with No 519 Sqn from September 1943 through to October 1944, and it is seen here at Skitten, in Scotland, in the summer of 1944. This unit flew meteorological missions over the North Atlantic and North Sea. FN966 was replaced by a Fortress II in October 1944, after which it was sent to the Empire Central Flying School. The bomber was finally struck off charge on 3 August 1946 (*D L Turner and crew via VMAF*)

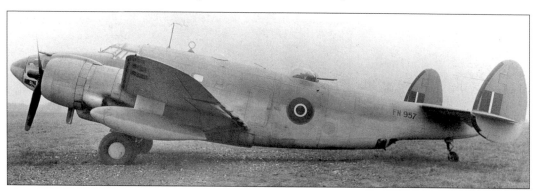

agents and supplies to underground forces in Europe, while No 299 Sqn flew Ventura I/IIs between November 1943 and January 1944, when they were replaced by Short Stirling IVs.

BRITISH COMMONWEALTH SQUADRONS

During the war, the British diverted a considerable number of Venturas to its dominion forces throughout the world. Over 260 Ventura Is and IIs were received by the Royal Canadian Air Force (RCAF) and the South African Air Force (SAAF), for example. In addition, during the

Several South African Air Force (SAAF) units flew the Ventura on ASW and convoy patrols between 1943 and 1945, this particular example (GR V FN957) serving with No 22 Sqn in the Mediterranean in 1943. Prior to being issued to the SAAF, FN957 had served with the Telecommunications Flying Unit, the A&AEE and No 11 Ferry Unit (*via Bruce Robertson*)

production run of the PV-1, a further 325 aircraft were delivered to the RAAF, RCAF, RNZAF and SAAF.

In February 1942, No 459 Sqn RAAF was commissioned in Egypt, where it operated Hudsons and Blenheims against German shipping in the eastern Mediterranean. In December of the following year it re-equipped with Venturas and, in conjunction with Hudsons, began bombing operations against targets in Greece and Crete. The unit's experience with the Ventura would last for less than seven months, however, for in July 1944 the unit was re-equipped with the Martin Baltimore.

Ventura I/IIs and GR Vs were used by the SAAF in the Mediterranean for convoy escort duties and anti-submarine patrols, No 17 Sqn converted to GR Vs from Blenheim Vs in May 1943. Five months later the unit moved to St Jean and Ramat David airfields, in Palestine, with detachments operating from Gibraltar and Bone, in Algeria. In July 1944 No 17 Sqn moved to Sardinia, returning to North Africa again in 1945.

No 22 Sqn SAAF converted to Venturas from Ju 86s and Avro Ansons in August 1942, the unit being based in Gibraltar and Egypt. No 25 Sqn SAAF converted to Venturas in September 1942 at Port Elizabeth, and in June 1944 the unit moved to Italy, where the Venturas were replaced by B-26 Marauders in November. Finally, No 27 Sqn SAAF flew Ventura GR Vs on convoy and anti-submarine patrols along the west coast of South Africa, and in March 1944 it began operations in the western Mediterranean and Spanish coastal areas.

ROYAL CANADIAN AIR FORCE

The Canadians equipped five Bomber Reconnaissance (BR) units with Venturas, mainly GR Vs – Nos 8, 113, 115, 145 and 149 Sqns. These

Personnel of No 145 Sqn RCAF pose both on, and in front of, Ventura 2184 'C' in June 1945. The unit's CO at the time was Wg Cdr J D Patterson. No 145 Sqn spent its entire war flying convoy patrols out of Dartmouth, Nova Scotia, after receiving Venturas in May 1943 (*Jack McManus Sr via VMAF*)

Venturas 2192, 2197 and 2199 (only partially visible) of No 149 Sqn await their crews whilst on detached duty at Smithers, British Columbia. The unit lost aircraft 2193 and its crew whilst flying from this base when 21-year-old Plt Off G C Mitchell crashed on Duke Island. Two of the crew survived the accident, but they were too severely injured to leave the wreckage. They finally succumbed to their injuries 16 days later. Although RCAF Venturas never encountered the enemy, they performed valuable service flying ASW patrols over the North Atlantic and Pacific, as well as protecting convoys. The Ventura served with the RCAF from June 1942 to April 1947, some 21 Mk Is, 108 Mk IIs and 157 GR Vs being used during this period (*Bill Horton via VMAF*)

Flying patrols over the vast expanses of the North Atlantic, Ventura crews were sometimes faced with the prospect of ditching in the frigid water. These crewmen are trying on early immersion suits whilst serving with RCAF Eastern Air Command on 23 March 1945 (*National Archives of Canada*)

Below
Decorated with elaborate artwork, this war-weary RCAF Ventura II was photographed in storage at Stanley, Nova Scotia, in 1944. Note its crudely painted roundel (*Bill Horton via VMAF*)

Bottom
GR V 2263 endured a wheels up landing at RCAF Port Hardy, in British Columbia, on 2 February 1944. A large number of Venturas were damaged or destroyed in take-off and landing accidents in the adverse weather conditions that aircrews frequently encountered in the Pacific Northwest. Post-war, most RCAF Venturas were scrapped or converted into civilian transports (*VMAF*)

units were primarily used for convoy coverage and anti-submarine patrols. No 8 'Ox' Sqn was designated as a bomber reconnaissance unit on 31 October 1940, and it went on to serve in Alaska in 1942–43, before eventually disbanding on 25 May 1945 at Patricia Bay, in British Columbia.

On the East Coast, No 113 was formed on 15 February 1942 and received Venturas in April 1943. The unit was based at Yarmouth, Nova Scotia, until disbanded on 23 August 1944. No 115 'Lynx' Sqn was formed in August 1941, and served in British Columbia until disbanded on 23 August 1944. Finally, No 149 'Sea Wolf' Sqn served as a torpedo-bomber unit pre-war, but was redesignated a bomber reconnaissance squadron on 15 March 1943. Deployed to Annette Island, Alaska, the unit served with the Canadian Western Air Command until disbanded at Terrace, British Columbia, on 15 March 1944.

PACIFIC OPS 1943–45

US Navy and Marine PV-1/2s ranged across the Pacific Ocean from the Aleutian Islands in the north to Guadalcanal in the south, flying armed reconnaissance missions between March 1943 and August 1945. Some 16 Navy PV-1 Ventura and PV-2 Harpoon squadrons participated in the war against Japan, namely VB/VPB (Navy Bombing/Navy Patrol Bombing Squadrons) 128, 130, 133, 135, 136, 137, 138, 139, 140, 142, 144, 146, 150, 151, 152 and 153. These units were all controlled by Fleet Air Wings (FAW), which dictated the activities of individual squadrons.

THE ALEUTIANS

PV-1 operations began in the North Pacific in the spring of 1943 when VB-135, commanded by Lt Cdr P C Williams, was sent into the front line. After training at Whidbey Island, Washington, the squadron arrived on Adak, in the Aleutians, on 12 April, and commenced operations soon after as part of FAW-4.

Cold, isolated and barren, the Aleutians are a chain of islands located in the North Pacific that extend south-west and north-west for over 1000 miles (1609 km). The land mass consists of 14 large and 55 smaller islands, each of which feature innumerable islets. If put altogether, the islands occupy a land area of 6821 square miles. Blighted by appalling weather rolling straight off the Pacific, the Aleutians boasted some of the worst flying conditions encountered by Allied forces in World War 2. Ventura pilot Doug Birdsall of VB-139 was a veteran of the campaign:

'The Navy increased the allowable take-off weight of our PV-1s to 29,000 lbs [13,154 kg], then established a maximum gross take-off weight of 34,000 lbs [15,422 kg]. We flew them out of Attu at night-time off slush-covered Marston Mat runways at that weight!'

An early model PV-1 (possibly belonging to VB-135) is seen at Annette Island, on the southern tip of the Alexander Archipelago of south-eastern Alaska, in the summer of 1943. This aircraft is camouflaged in the Navy's standard blue/grey and light grey scheme. Note the low-hanging clouds over the mountains in the distance. Such weather conditions were the cause of numerous fatal Ventura crashes in-theatre when aircraft flew into cloud-shrouded mountains (*Murray Castator Collection via Larry Milberry/VMAF*)

A PV-1 of FAW-4 undergoes engine maintenance at Annette Island. Another early-delivery PV-1, this aircraft displays the national insignia used prior to 28 June 1943. Entry into the aircraft was made through the fuselage door to the left of the insignia (*Murray Castator Collection via Larry Milberry/VMAF*)

Adorned with fuselage art, an FAW-4 PV-1 taxies out at Annette Island at the start of yet another mission to the Aleutians (*Murray Castator Collection via Larry Milberry/VMAF*)

Flying over the frigid waters of the North Pacific, early-build PV-1s X-4, X-5 and 'Black 18' of VB-136 come home following a mission in mid-1943 (*via George Villasenor*)

Flying them on missions to the enemy-held Kurile Islands also posed a problem, for the PV-1's range was approximately 1600 miles (1609 km), while the distance to Paramushiro and back was near 1500 miles (2412 km). Birdsall continues:

'We ended up with 11 separate fuel tanks and no cross-feed capability, which meant that we had to burn each tank dry to utilise all of the fuel. After a few months, Lockheed came up and retro-fitted a cross-feed system.'

Two weeks after the arrival of VB-135, VB-136, led by Lt Cdr Nathan S Haines, became the second PV-1 unit to reach the Aleutians. Both units flew anti-submarine sweeps and photographic reconnaissance missions over the Japanese-held islands of Attu and Kiska.

On 5 May VB-135 moved to Amchitka, which enjoyed the same kind of weather experienced by the rest of the Western Aleutian Islands – fog, rain and snow, with temperatures ranging from 11°F to 65°F throughout the year. It was a miserable place to be posted to, and many missions were scrubbed due to poor weather. However, the new base was within bombing range of Kiska, and the ASD-1 radar-equipped Venturas were used to guide USAAF B-24s to their targets. In August, VB-135 moved to Alexai Point, on Attu, after the island was retaken by the US Army in May.

In October 1943 VB-136 joined its sister-squadrons on Attu and commenced anti-aircraft searches. Two contacts were soon made with enemy aircraft, and the unit's Lt Dinsmore duly damaged a Mitsubishi G4M 'Betty' bomber. In November VB-135 was relieved, transferring back to Whidbey

Island. Losses for the squadron in-theatre had been light, with only two fatalities occurring in an operational accident. The same could not be said for the PV-1s however – of the 15 aircraft originally taken north by the unit, only four remained airworthy by the end of operations.

'EMPIRE EXPRESS'

By the late autumn of 1943, the US Navy's Commander-in-Chief Pacific (CINCPAC) was keen to gauge the strength of Japanese military assets in the northern Kurile Islands prior to committing to an American invasion. CINCPAC ordered Commodore Leslie E Gehres, commanding officer of FAW-4, to initiate photographic reconnaissance missions of the area, which were dubbed the 'Empire Express' by participating crews. The first such mission was flown on 16 November 1943 by a PV-1 from VB-136, captained by Lt H K Mantius.

The Ventura had to be modified to fulfil this tasking, with special racks being installed to carry four one million candle power photo-flash bombs. These were used to light up the target for the K-19A cameras fitted in the bomber's nose. The Kuriles were 650 miles (1045 km) from Attu, so a US 280-gallon fuel tank was installed in the aft bomb-bay. To offset this extra weight, the aft armour plating and the tunnel guns were removed. Nevertheless, these modifications made the PV-1 some 3000 lbs (1361 kg) heavier. Consequently, several aeroplanes crashed trying to take off, killing the crews.

In mid-December 1943 VB-136 was relieved by VB-139, commanded by Lt Cdr L R Stevens. The new unit arrived during the winter, when runways froze solid and precipitation blanked out the base. For the next six months VB-139 continued night photographic missions to the Kuriles – the men of this unit were taking part in a war that very few people in the United States had heard about.

Snowing was falling on Attu on 25 March 1944 when five of the unit's PV-1s prepared to take off for a strike on Japanese installations in the northern Kurile Islands. Will R Swinney, radio/radarman flying with Lt Boris Georgeff, recalls the mission:

'It was a five-aeroplane operation against Kokutan Zaki, on Paramushiro, with our CO, Lt Cdr W R Stevens, leading the first bomber. The second aeroplane was piloted by the squadron's executive officer, A G Neal. Following in third, fourth and fifth places were Q E Norem, W S Whitman and J H Moore.

'This flight was jinxed from the word go thanks to an incorrect weather report given during a pre-flight briefing. Moore's aeroplane accelerated down the runway but crashed into Massacre Bay just moments after take-off, killing four of the seven-man crew. Stevens turned back several hours into the mission when both his engines began failing, but the remaining PV-1s pressed on and overshot the target. Approaching the USSR, they made a 180-degree turn, dropped their bombs and headed home.'

Also seen on the previous page, Venturas X-4, X-5 and Black 18 fly over typically rugged, and snow-covered, topography in the Aleutians Islands in 1943 (*George Villasenor*)

Commanding officer of VB-139, Lt Cdr W R Stevens (left), and Lt Cdr A G Neal, his executive officer, stand beside a Ventura decorated with the FAW-4 logo (and six mission decals) on 4 June 1944. Navy Ventura units based in the Aleutians were nicknamed 'The Bats' because of their nocturnal night reconnaissance missions to the Kurile Islands (*NARA*)

X-13 of VB-136 is refuelled in the open for a forthcoming strike in early 1944. This unit was the second to operate PV-1s in the Aleutians, and it completed two combat tours (*via George Villasenor*)

Whitman's aeroplane was seen by a radar operator in another PV-1 to drop its bombs and turn towards Attu. Then, without explanation, his aircraft made a 180-degree turn and headed back to Paramushiro. The last words transmitted by Whitman were, 'Down, down!' Will Swinney and other squadron personnel thought that the crew had been captured, although neither Whitman or his crew were ever seen again.

The mystery was solved 56 years later in 2000, when the wreckage of Whitman's aeroplane and the remains of its crew were found on the slopes of the Mutnovsky volcano on the Kamchatka Peninsula. The wreckage of the PV-1 had first been spotted in 1962 by Soviet geologists, but due to the Cold War information of their find was not forwarded to the United States for some 38 years.

The Aleutian weather claimed almost as many lives and aircraft as the Japanese did, with VB-139 losing four Venturas in operational accidents. Two of these aircraft had been lost on the 25 March mission, which resulted in the deaths of ten men. However, despite these adverse conditions, the unit successfully flew 78 photographic and bombing missions before being relieved by VB-135 (led by Lt Cdr P L Stahl) on 5 May.

The 'Empire Express' continued with night photo and bombing missions, Commodore Leslie Gehres now referring to the Air Wing in his media reports as 'The Bats' because most of the missions that VB-135 flew were conducted at night. From 5 May to 12 June, weather permitting, the squadron sent four to eight PV-1s on bombing and photo-reconnaissance missions to the Kuriles. Such missions were hazardous, and VB-135 lost three aircraft and crews.

The first of these flights commenced on the evening of 5–6 May, when nine PV-1s took off and headed for Kashiwabara airfield, on Paramushiro. The weather near the target was heavily overcast, and six of the Venturas could not find the target and returned to Attu. The lead aeroplane (BuNo 48733), piloted by Lt A A Wheat, failed to return, the PV-1 almost certainly being shot down by heavy and accurate anti-aircraft fire. Another Ventura piloted by Lt Clark managed to find the target, and the crew salvoed its payload from 9000 ft (2743 m). Two extremely close bursts of flak then flipped the aeroplane onto its back, and Clark had to use all his strength to right the bomber.

In June 1944, the primary mission for the PV-1 squadrons changed from reconnaissance to harassing raids against Japanese installations in the Kuriles. On the 11th Lt J P Vivian discovered an airfield on Shimushu Island chocked full of torpedo-armed G4M 'Betty' bombers. The

following day, Lt M A 'Butch' Mason, Executive Officer of VB-135, led six Venturas on a bombing mission against the airfield. Attacking at low level, the PV-1s devastated the airfield with 500-lb (227-kg) general-purpose bombs before returning safely to Attu.

Three days later six Venturas performed a diversionary strike against Miyoshino airfield on Shimushu while Lt Patteson undertook a photo-recce sortie over the rest of Shimushu, and Paramushiro. Patteson approached his first target, Kataoka, at 11,000 ft (3352 m) and began taking photographs. As the PV-1 neared the second target, two A6M Zeke fighters intercepted the bomber, but they were quickly driven off by AOM Jacobson's top turret guns. The sortie's final target was Karabu Zaki, on the southern tip of Paramushiro, and several fighters again intercepted the Ventura. Lt Patteson was forced to dive down to 8000 ft (2438 m), increasing the power to the engines as he went. This time the turret gunner claimed hits on one of the fighters, and the PV-1 raced home unscathed, but in need of two new engines.

Of the six PV-1s that had taken part in this mission, two were forced to land in the USSR, where the crews were interned. Lt Patteson repeated the flight on 25 June, and was attacked by 11 fighters – the turret gunner was duly credited with one kill and one probable. The pilot was awarded two Distinguished Flying Crosses and two Air Medals for the successful completion of these missions.

On 17 June, VB-136 returned to the action under the command of Lt Cdr Charles Wayne. The unit's PV-1s were heavily modified with new navigational instruments, such as LORAN (LOng-RAnge Navigation), as well as a chin package with an additional three 0.50-cal machine guns.

VB-135 sustained another loss on 23 July when Lt Vivian sank an armed picket boat. His PV-1 sustained damage during the engagement, however, and he landed in the USSR, where the crew was interned.

On 7 September, Lts 'Butch' Mason and Sparks made a daylight raid on the dockyards at Kakumabetsu. Nearing the target, a small ship was observed, and Mason made three strafing attacks. The attack alerted anti-aircraft gun positions, and as the XO pickled off three 500-lb (227-kg) general purpose bombs, which destroyed several docks, a 20 mm gun position opened up and hit the PV-1. Mason's co-pilot sustained a deep gash near his temple and

This anonymous PV-1 is parked in a damp dispersal area at RCAF Port Hardy, in British Columbia, in 1944 (*Jim Deacon via VMAF*)

A pair of VB-135 Venturas head for Paramushiro, in the Kurile Islands, in July 1944. BuNo 48936 has the last three digits of its identity painted in white on the rear fuselage, along with its squadron number (10) in black aft of the turret. This photograph was taken during the unit's second tour in the Aleutians. Due to the Ventura's impressive range, no American fighters in-theatre were capable of escorting them to their targets, so the bomber crews had to fend for themselves. On one such occasion, when Lt J W Pool of VB-135 was engaged by eight 'Tojo' fighters over Shimushu, in the Kurile Islands, the PV-1 pilot succeeded in shooting one Ki-44 down and then outrunning the remaining seven at low level (*via USN*)

another crewman was hit by shrapnel under the eye. A fire also broke out in the nose compartment and began filling the cockpit with smoke, although the navigator quickly put it out and the PV-1 returned to base.

On 12 September, Venturas of VB-136 attacked installations on Shimushu. Lts Moorehead and Bacak approached the target from an altitude of just 50 ft, and hit several buildings with 500-lb (227-kg) bombs. Enemy fighters – 'Hamps' (a variant of the A6M) and Ki-43 'Oscars' – then appeared, but Moorehead outran them by accelerating the Ventura to 320 mph (514 km/h).

Two days later, Lts Morrison and Littleton bombed a cannery and fishery on the eastern coast of Paramushiro, and after he had dropped his ordnance four 'Tojo' fighters attacked Littleton. He turned to starboard and placed two fighters in front of his nose guns, whereupon he fired and hit one of the Ki-44s. The fighter pulled up and the turret gunner then hit him with further rounds, and sent the 'Tojo' crashed in flames. A second fighter then attacked and Littleton pushed the PV-1 over into a dive, levelling off just 20 ft (6 m) above the water. He then outran the remaining Ki-44s.

On 17 September, Lt Cdr Wayne's PV-1 was damaged over Paramushiro, and he too was forced to land in the USSR. The loss of VB-136's CO, and an increase in heavy anti-aircraft fire and fighters, forced Commodore Gehres to halt 'Empire Express' runs for several weeks. The unit spent the rest of its tour flying sector searches and night reconnaissance missions until relieved by VPB-131 – on 1 October all Navy bomber units had been re-designated Patrol and Bombing squadrons (VPB).

MISSIONS RESUME

VPB-131 arrived in-theatre on 22 October, this unit having previously seen action on the Atlantic coast flying PV-1s from bases in the Caribbean. In May 1944 the unit reformed at Whidbey Island under the command of Lt Cdr Rolland Hastreiter, and as with VPB-136, its Venturas were modified with chin guns, LORAN and ASD-1 radar.

On 4 November 1944 the VPB-131 flew its first strike when four PV-1s performed a diversionary attack while Eleventh Air Force B-24s hit the primary target of Karabu. The diversion worked, for six enemy fighters bounced the Venturas. In the melee which ensued, Lt Ellingboe's aircraft was shot down, killing all on board. The remaining PV-1s managed to fight their way out, and one fighter was claimed destroyed.

Through November and December, both VPB-131 and -136 flew regular anti-shipping sweeps and night reconnaissance missions without incident.

From January 1945, VPB-131 began using 5-in HVARs against enemy positions in the Kuriles. These hard-hitting rockets were used to great effect on the 24th,

Snow blankets the airfield at Casco Cove, on Attu Island, in late 1944. Snow storms in the winter and fog during the remaining months of the year made flying in the Aleutians extremely difficult. Indeed, operational losses due to weather inflicted more casualties on FAW-4 than combat with the Japanese (*via George Villasenor*)

This artwork adorned a Navy Ventura seen at Smithers, in British Columbia, in the spring of 1945 (*David R Boan*)

A torpedo is manhandled into position beneath a PV-2 of VPB-139 during a snowstorm. Quite why this weapon was loaded remains a mystery, for the unit never flew any torpedo attacks (*via G Villasenor*)

Barren, snow-covered hills rise behind Harpoon 36 of VPB-139 in the early spring of 1945. With a longer range, PV-2s took over the majority of bombing missions to the Kurile Islands from PV-1s (*via G Villasenor*)

when Lt Cdr Hastreiter led four PV-1s against a lighthouse and radio station on Kotuton Zaki. From a height of 1000 ft (304 m), the squadron CO launched all eight of his rockets and scored hits on the base of the lighthouse. The remaining three PV-1s also launched their rockets and claimed a further ten strikes on radio towers and a radio station.

Rocket attacks continued as Hastreiter led four Venturas against Kurabu Zaki a few days later. After firing his rockets at a radar installation, he discovered a column of Japanese troops marching down the road, and his attack killed or wound many of them. Following behind the CO, Lt Newby also salvoed off four pairs of rockets at a radar site. The first HVARs passed through the radar screen, while the second and third salvoes missed. However, the fourth pair hit the base of the radar screen, destroying the station. As Newby pulled up, his PV-1 clipped the top of a hill behind the radar site, tearing a hole in the starboard wingtip.

On 22 February the unit suffered its first operational loss when Lt Powers and his crew were forced to bail out over the USSR. As with other Ventura crews before them, they were interned. For the rest of the month, and into March, fisheries and canneries became VPB-131's favourite targets.

PV-2 HARPOON OPERATIONS

With the arrival of VPB-139 and its PV-2 Harpoons, which had a greater range, the PV-1s of VPB-131 were regulated to routine search sectors. VPB-139 was the first PV-2-equipped unit to see combat, the unit having reformed with Lt Cdr Glenn A David as its CO in February 1945. By 12 March all of its aircraft had arrived at Attu, and after relieving VPB-136, VPB-139 crews began familiarising themselves with combat conditions in the Aleutians. On 6 April the Harpoon made its long-awaited combat debut against the Japanese with a rocket attack on Kokutan Zaki.

Later that same month problems with the PV-2's wing spar forced the unit to modify its combat operations. Unable to manoeuvre vigorously for fear of suffering total wing failure, Harpoons could now only be operated in areas where enemy fighters were not expected, and weather conditions were deemed to be benign.

On 10 May, eight PV-2s attacked radar installations at Minami Zaki, and they were greeted by heavy flak. Three aircraft were seriously damaged. By June there were very few targets left that were worth attacking, although the Japanese could still put up a fight when American aircraft appeared overhead. Will Swinney recalls a typical Harpoon mission:

'A flight was organised on 6 June, with Lt Georgeff as flight leader. He and Lt(jg) Daniel were to search the east coast of Shimushu, Paramishier and Paramushiro Straits, but the aeroplanes became separated en route and were unable to make contact again.

'Lt Georgeff made landfall on Cape Lopatka and headed down the east coast of Shimushu at an altitude of 300 ft (91m). When he reached a point about four miles north-east of Torishima Retto, an "Oscar" was

A PV-2 from VPB-139 is refuelled at Attu before conducting a strike on the Kurile Islands in April 1945. Note the mounting brackets for the underwing 5-in HVARs above the heads of the refuelling crew (*via George Villasenor*)

Visible as little more than a speck immediately above the formation of the three VPB-139 PV-2s, a P-38 Lightning peels away from the bombers after safely escorting them back to Attu following a strike on the Kurile Islands (*via George Villasenor*)

The pilot of Harpoon 26 runs up his engines prior to signalling for the chocks to be removed so that he can taxi out at the start of another mission. Note the eight 5-in HVARs beneath the wings outboard of the external fuel tanks. Barely visible below a blanket of ice and snow is the airfield's Marston matting. The PV-2 had a longer range than the PV-1 but a lower top speed due to its increased weight. The first Harpoons left the assembly line from the Vega factory in late 1944, although design problems delayed the type's combat debut until April 1945 (*via George Villasenor*)

sighted about three miles away at an altitude of 500 ft (152 m), closing at 090 degrees towards the Harpoon.

'Lt Georgeff immediately altered his course, increased speed to 240 knots (276 mph or 444km/h) and went down to 100 ft (30 m) "on the deck". The enemy fighter easily closed to within 1500 ft (457 m), remaining on a parallel course for about seven minutes, then made a flat run at the Harpoon. Splashes were seen in the water short of the PV-2, but no tracers were observed. Upon completing the run, the "Oscar" pulled up sharply and was lost in cloud cover, not to be seen again. The Harpoon maintained full power for ten minutes as Lt Georgeff set course for base.

'Approaching Cape Lopatka, Lt(jg) Daniel continued down the eastern coast of Shimushu. At an altitude of 3000 ft (914 m), he sighted Masugawa on the starboard and observed two open fishing boats and a

grounded deep-sea fishing boat just south of this point. A sharp turn was made to port and the boats were strafed. Continuing the turn, buildings on Masugawa were also strafed. Pulling up into a tight turn to starboard, Daniel attacked the fishing boats once again.

'Making another tight turn to port, one bomb was dropped from an altitude of 300 ft (91m), exploding behind the main fishery buildings, and sending up a cloud of debris from a pile of stacked lumber. A complete 360-degree turn was then made at the same altitude, and a bomb was dropped, exploding among the boats. One final strafing run was made, and Lt(jg) Daniel then set course for home after having fired a total of 1125 rounds and dropping three bombs on various targets.'

Bombing of radar installations, canneries and fisheries continued through July, with minimal interference from enemy fighters. On 10 August VPB-139 was relieved by VPB-135.

During 'Empire Express', PV-1 units lost 34 aircraft – VB-131 three, -135 fifteen, -136 eight and -139 six on its first tour and two on its second. Many of those lost landed in the USSR after being damaged in action, while others were written off on landing, skidding on the ice-covered, steel-matted, runways in-theatre.

GUADALCANAL TO OWI

By the spring of 1943, both allied and Japanese forces were exhausted after months of bitter fighting in the South and Central Pacific. Another four months would pass before Japanese defences would be tested once again by another big Allied push. For now, it was a time for the Japanese to rebuild their aerial strength and fortify their positions in New Georgia, the Bismarcks and the Admiralties. For the Americans, and their Australian and New Zealand allies, fighting would continue in New Guinea while military planners formulated the next offensive that would ultimately see the liberation of the Philippines.

For such an advance to take place, the Japanese fortress of Rabaul had to be either invaded or neutralised. The Americans needed advanced air and naval bases to launch such an attack, so the first step in the campaign was to take nearby New Georgia. By late June 1943, US forces in-theatre had been bolstered sufficiently to allow offensive operations to commence. On the 21st Operation *Toenails* – the invasion of New Georgia – began with the first landing at Segi Point.

The landing force met only light opposition, and within a week US Navy SeaBees were building a new airstrip. August 1943 was the climactic month for the New Georgia campaign, with the capture of Munda and the battle of Vella Gulf, with Vella Lavella and Lae soon to follow. Operating from these new airfields were American and New Zealand Ventura squadrons.

FIRST IN THE SOUTH PACIFIC

In August 1943 VB-140 (led by Lt Cdr Vernon Williams) became the first PV-1 unit to go into combat in the South Pacific. Controlled by Strike Command, Commander Air Solomons, the squadron was split into two detachments within days of its arrival at Espiritu Santo. One det went to Henderson Field, on Guadalcanal, and the other to Munda.

One of VB-140's most memorable missions occurred on 16 November when seven PV-1s flew through the narrow straits of Buka Passage. The unit had waited four days for the weather to break, and thus give it the chance to lay mines in the narrow neck of water that the Japanese used to reinforce their men at Bougainville.

As they approached the drop point for the mines, the Venturas, flying at an altitude of 700 ft (213 m), ran through a gauntlet of anti-aircraft fire from the gun emplacements that protected the passage. Led by Lt Cdr Charles Houston, executive officer of VB-140, the Venturas flew through the passage at just 160 knots (184 mph or 296 km/h), each aeroplane dropping its 1900-lb (862-kg) mine at its scheduled time so that the straits would be evenly sowed with these lethal weapons.

As one Ventura swung out of its flak-studded course at the end of the channel, it narrowly missed colliding with another PV-1. Ken Sanford, co-pilot of *The Streaking Angel* (BuNo 33228), had just closed the bomb-bay doors as his pilot, Lt James 'Bach' Bachmeier, pushed the throttles forward to get out of range of the flak. Sanford remembers:

'A flash from a burst suddenly revealed a PV-1 on a collision course, and Bachmeier pulled back the throttles, pushed the yoke forward and veered off to the left, missing the other aircraft by a breath. Bach muttered, "Shit – that was close". We then joined up for the trip home, somewhat subdued by the thought that we had just missed joining up forever.'

They were not out of danger yet though, as seconds later Bachmeier had to make a violent manoeuvre to avoid hitting a parachute attached to a mine as it descended. In the wake of this mission, participating crews became known as the 'Buka Passage Kids'. Ken Sanford later commanded PB4Y-2 Privateer unit VPB-123.

During VB-140's tour of duty, it lost just one aircraft and its crew. On 12 October the unit had attacked Ballale Island, and during the course of the mission Lt Anthony Brenner and his crew had exhibited extreme bravery by overflying the target twice. On their first attempt they had been put off by heavy flak that protected the island airstrip, so Brenner swung around and headed for the target once again. This time he faced even more opposition, but he nevertheless pressed home his attack at low level and hit the target. Exactly one week later, Lt Brenner and his crew disappeared on a similar bombing mission to Ballale.

In seven months of combat, VB-140 had flown 664 sorties. After returning to the US on 8 April 1944, the unit reformed as VPB-123, equipped with the PB4Y-2 Privateer.

A VB-138 Ventura is seen in its spartan revetment on Guadalcanal in 1943. This unit was only the second Navy PV-1 squadron to see service in the South Pacific. The aircraft is painted in the standard blue-grey and light grey Navy scheme (*via F T Pierce*)

NEXT UP

VB-138 (led by Lt Cdr Murray Hanson) was the next PV-1 unit to taste combat in the South Pacific. The squadron had suffered 11 fatalities in the build up to its deployment – Lt(jg) D L Lough crashed his Ventura into Mt Washington in May 1943, killing the crew of five, and on 6 July another aeroplane crashed into the sea off Hawaii, killing six.

Between 12 July and 10 August, VB-138 was assigned to Canton, in the Ellice Islands, from where it flew reconnaissance missions to the Japanese-held Gilbert Islands. No enemy activity was detected in the region, so the squadron moved back to Kaneohe, in Hawaii, until October, when orders were issued sending it to the Russell Islands. From here the unit would engage enemy forces in New Ireland, New Britain and Rabaul.

During the unit's move back into the front line, co-pilot Lt F T Pierce survived a hair-raising episode in his

PV-1 when it lost an engine taking off from Fiji at the start of VB-138's move up to the Solomons.

'The PV-1 was a difficult aeroplane to fly on two good engines when at take-off weight, and the loss of a Double Wasp on take-off resulted in many accidents and deaths. Our right engine stopped just as the wheels left the uneven surface of the runway ground. We had two full 150-gallon drop tanks, and I tried to jettison them – the right tank dropped but the left one would not. We had a dead engine and one drop tank. The pilot managed to bring the aeroplane around, and we burned off fuel for about 45 minutes before coming in to land. On the approach, the wings grazed some palm trees, but we managed to make a downwind landing without a problem.'

NEW BRITAIN

In December 1943 the New Britain campaign was launched, with landings taking place at Arawe, followed by Cape Gloucester. New Britain is a mountainous, heavily forested land mass some 250 miles in length. The main Japanese base of Rabaul was located on the Gazelle Peninsula, and with an estimated strength of 80,000 to 90,000 troops and 201 operational aircraft, it became the focus of Allied air attacks. Prior to the landings, a series of air attacks had been launched against the base on 12 October, with Gen George Kenney's Fifth Air Force despatching over 300 aircraft to pound the Japanese fortress.

During the months to come, personnel and supplies on Rabaul would be considerably reduced. Amongst the hardest hit were the fighter squadrons sent up to protect their base against allied aircraft. Their A6M5 Zeros proved to be no match for the Navy's F4U Corsairs and F6F Hellcats, and by February 1944 Rabaul's air strength had been reduced to just 15 grounded Zeros and a dozen or so patrol and reconnaissance aircraft.

On 3 April 1944, VB-148 arrived on Munda and was placed under the operational control of FAW-1. Immediately, the unit began providing fighter cover for C-47 transports carrying US Army paratroopers to New Guinea. Additionally, it continued with the harassing missions that sister PV-1 squadrons had conducted over Bougainville.

Prior to reaching the front line, VB-148 had trained at Vernalis Naval Air Station, approximately 15 miles (24 km) south-east of Modesto, in California. It was the first PV-1 unit to receive 5-in rocket rails (three under each wing) for HVARs, and these had been bore-sighted, and the pilots trained in how to use them for attacks on shipping, whilst at Inyokern, also in California.

The unit's gunnery officer was Lt Perry Ustick, a veteran US Naval Reserve officer who had joined VB-148 in August 1943 after recovering from a bout of malaria. He had been infected with the disease at Guadalcanal in December 1942 after the fourth battle of Savo Island. Ustick had been lucky to survive the battle, having been aloft in an OS2U Kingfisher seaplane when his ship, the cruiser USS *Northampton* (CA-26), had been sunk by the Japanese during the Savo engagement.

Now fully recovered from his sickness, Lt Ustick had been charged with working up tactics for attacking targets with the PV-1's rocket armament:

'I devised a method of dive-bombing the target at a 20-degree angle, firing our rockets at 1900 ft (579 m), our two 0.50-cal (12.7 mm) nose

The crew of VB-138 PV-1 'Black 18' pose at Guadalcanal in 1943. Early production models such as this one did not have dual controls, leaving the co-pilot to wonder what his role was in the aircraft! (*via F T Pierce*)

Co-pilot Lt F T Pierce is seen with the Disney-originated *Donald Duck* artwork that adorned his aircraft during his tour with VB-138. Such decoration was commonplace on PV-1s in the Pacific (*via F T Pierce*)

guns at 1000 ft (304 m) and dropping a 500-lb (227-kg) general-purpose bomb at 700 ft (213 m). As I recall, our speed was close to 300 knots (345 mph or 555 km/h) in the dive. I demonstrated this attack method for some dignitaries that came out from the Pentagon to Kaneohe, where we were training prior to deploying to the forward area. I brought them up to the cockpit so they could see the whole attack method. They were duly impressed, especially when I hit the target with rockets, guns and a bomb at 300 knots.'

The PV-1 was both fast and heavily armed, but it could also be tricky to fly, especially when it was overloaded. Lt Ustick recalls leaving Kaneohe when the VB-148 deployed to the South Pacific:

'Getting our overloaded aeroplanes off of the 7000-ft (2133m) Marston mat airfield at Kaneohe was quite an achievement. We were loaded to 33,000 lbs (14,969 kg), which was maximum gross overload, with full internal and wing fuel tanks, drop tanks and all of our luggage, spare parts and even a box marked "Physical Education Gear", which was in fact liquor for the Officers' mess that we had bought in San Francisco before we left the States! We also stuffed the enlisted personnels' duffel bags into the nose cone.

'When it was my turn to take off, I went down to the farthest corner of the mat, checked my mags and started my roll. As I picked up speed and hit 80 knots (92 mph or 148 km/h), I felt she wanted to fly so I eased back on the yoke to lift off and popped the gear up to reduce drag and to pick up single engine speed. However, she wanted to fly back down to the runway. I couldn't lift the nose. Now the end of the runway was coming up and I had too much speed to stop. I suddenly figured I needed some nose up tab, and I reached for the tab wheel and gave it a good nose-up turn. I started to fly after my wheels hit the dirt area between the mat and a road. Later, I realised that in my excitement I had cranked in about three or four degrees of nose-down tab when I was trying to get the tail up at the beginning of my take-off run! I skimmed over a hill by no more than 25–50 ft (7–15 m), and then I was out over that beautiful flat Pacific Ocean.'

EARLY COMBAT LOSS

On one of VP-148's first rocket attacks, on 14 April 1944, a PV-1 flown by Lt William T Henderson was shot up over Kahili airfield by anti-aircraft fire, wounding two of the crew. Henderson managed to ditch the Ventura four miles east of Ballale Island, and four of the five-man crew made it into a raft – the top turret gunner, who was wounded, went down with the PV-1. Shortly after scrambling into the raft, the second wounded man died, and the remaining three crewmen were rescued by a PBY. Nineteen days later PV-1 BuNo 34824 was lost when Lt William E Davis and his crew failed to return from a patrol to Bougainville.

On 21 May VB-148 moved to Emirau, in the Treasury Islands, and began anti-shipping sweeps of the western-most land mass in the Caroline Islands chain. Located some 250 miles (402 km) south of Rabaul and 600 miles (965 km) south of Truk, the island is two miles (3 km) wide and eight miles (12 km) long, and runs in an east–west direction. It became the focus of military planners as a substitute target following the cancellation (on 12 March 1944) of the invasion of Kavieng by the Joint Chiefs of Staff.

Two airfields were specially built for bomber and fighter operations on Emirau, these being named Inshore and North Cape. At the end of each runway were cliffs that dropped 75 ft to 185 ft (22 m to 56 m) down to the sea, and these served to focus the minds of pilots taking off at night or in bad weather.

Whilst conducting patrols from their new base, crews from VB-148 engaged enemy aircraft on several occasions, and succeeded in downing two G4M 'Betty' bombers. The first of these fell to Lt Harry Metke during an interception south of Truk on 30 May, and a week later (on 7 June) squadron XO Lt Harry Stanford shot down the second 'Betty'.

The Japanese continued to try to supply their bases on New Britain and New Ireland by running small convoys during this period, and these were often spotted by patrolling PV-1s. On 26 July Lt Metke came across just such a convoy consisting of six ships, and after radioing in a contact report, he attacked. And although his PV-1 was armed with ASW depth bombs, Metke flew on through heavy flak, which wounded one of the crew, and succeeded in damaging two of the ships with his ordnance.

Later in the day, Lt Cdr Jakeman led six PV-1s in a low-level attack on the convoy which sank three vessels. VB-148 hit the surviving vessels once again the following day, when a fourth ship was sunk and a Ki-61 'Tony' fighter, attempting to defend the convoy, was shot down by Lt Van Wilber's turret gunner, Leonard Wheatley. In October, the unit headed back to the US after being relieved by No 3 Sqn RNZAF.

VB-146

The next PV-1 unit to be sent into action in the South Pacific was VB-146, commanded by Lt Cdr J P Robinson Jr. Commissioned on 15 July 1943 at NAS Whidbey Island's Ault Field, the unit suffered a bitter blow on 29 August 1943 when its first CO, Lt Cdr Ralph R Beachum, and his crew were posted missing on a training flight. In October 1994, a hiker found the wreckage of Beachum's PV-1 (BuNo 34637) on Mount Baker, near Seattle, Washington, and the remains of the crew were finally recovered.

Many of the squadron's senior pilots and enlisted crew members had come from PBY units VB-12 and VP-43, and after completing training, VB-146 arrived at Kaneohe in late December 1943. On 11 January 1944 the unit was assigned the Midway Patrol, with six aircraft and nine crews. Eleven days later the Johnston Island Patrol, and convoy coverage, was assigned to five aeroplanes and six crews, and these sorties lasted until 1 April. Later that month rocket rails were installed and calibration and training on how to use the 5-in HVARs was conducted. For the next two months VB-146 remained in Hawaii awaiting orders to the forward area.

On 8 June the unit commenced its deployment to the Seventh Fleet's area of operations, and on arrival at Pityilu Island, in the Admiralty group, VB-146 was assigned to the hunter-killer ASW group. In July, PBY Catalinas replaced the PV-1s in this capacity, and VB-146 was in turn given 400–500-mile search sectors to patrol from Pityilu. On 1 October 1944 the unit had its designation changed to VPB-l46, and 17 days later it moved to Morotai, where it reported to FAW-17.

Lying ten miles (16 km) north of Halmahera, the island of Morotai is 44 miles (70 km) long and 25 miles (40 km) wide. Except for a small coastal plain on the Gila Peninsula, it is a (*text continues on page 47*)

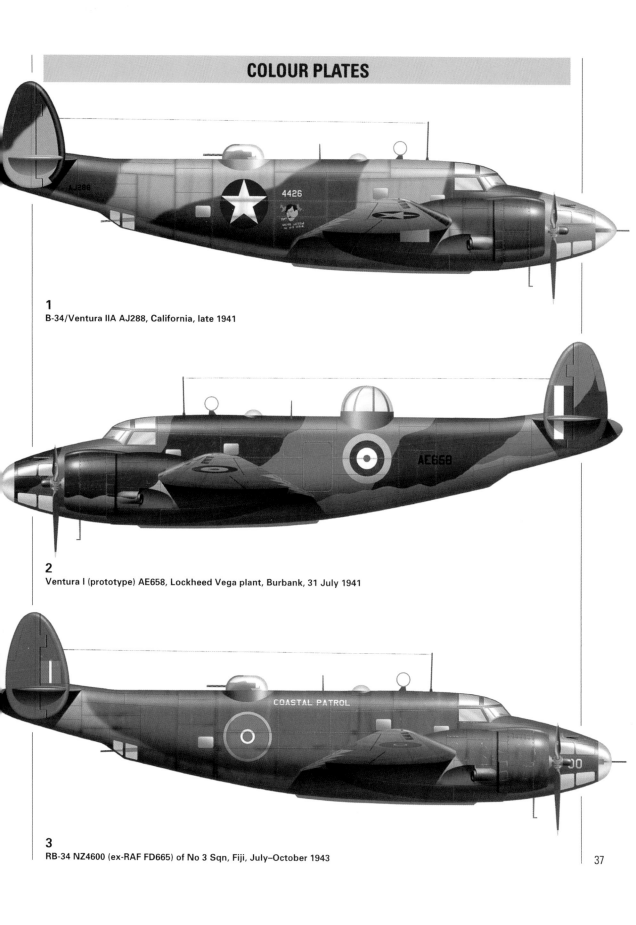

1
B-34/Ventura IIA AJ288, California, late 1941

2
Ventura I (prototype) AE658, Lockheed Vega plant, Burbank, 31 July 1941

3
RB-34 NZ4600 (ex-RAF FD665) of No 3 Sqn, Fiji, July–October 1943

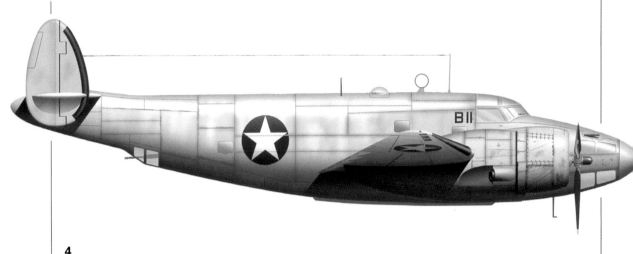

4
PV-3 'Black B-11' (BuNo unknown) of VP-82, Argentia, Newfoundland, October 1942

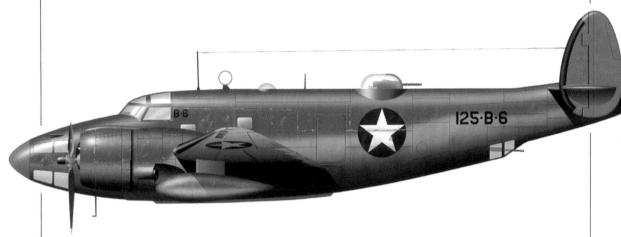

5
PV-1 'Black 125-B-6' (BuNo unknown) flown by Lt Thomas Kinaszczuk, VB-125, Argentia, Newfoundland, 27 April 1943

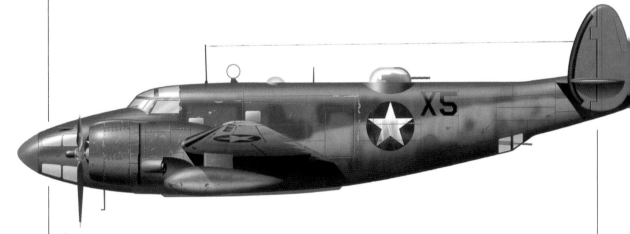

6
PV-1 'Black X5' (BuNo unknown) flown by Lt(jg) L W Fischer, VB-135, Attu, Alaska, June 1943

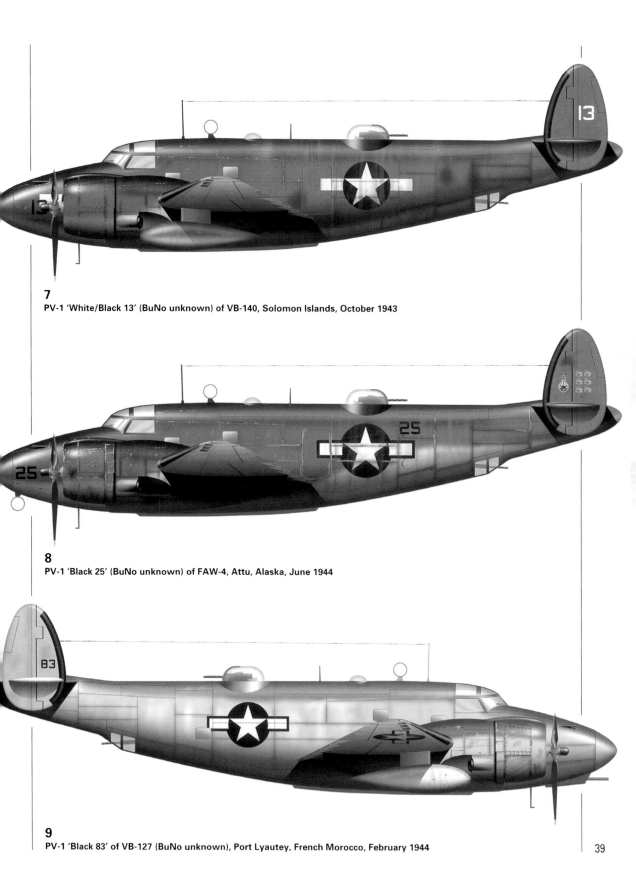

7
PV-1 'White/Black 13' (BuNo unknown) of VB-140, Solomon Islands, October 1943

8
PV-1 'Black 25' (BuNo unknown) of FAW-4, Attu, Alaska, June 1944

9
PV-1 'Black 83' of VB-127 (BuNo unknown), Port Lyautey, French Morocco, February 1944

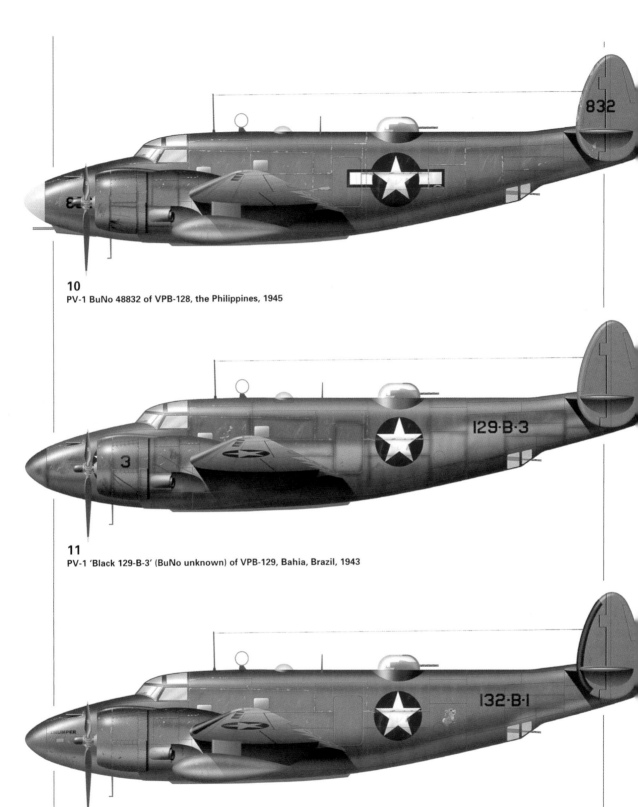

10
PV-1 BuNo 48832 of VPB-128, the Philippines, 1945

11
PV-1 'Black 129-B-3' (BuNo unknown) of VPB-129, Bahia, Brazil, 1943

12
PV-1 'Black 132-B-1' (BuNo unknown) flown by Lt Tidmarsh, VB-132, Port Lyautey, French Morocco, 1944

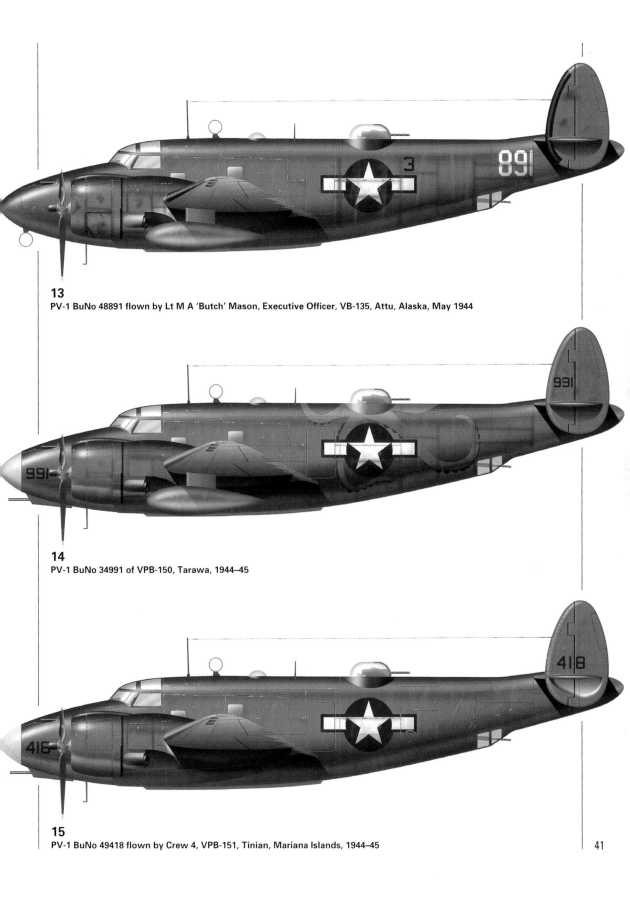

13
PV-1 BuNo 48891 flown by Lt M A 'Butch' Mason, Executive Officer, VB-135, Attu, Alaska, May 1944

14
PV-1 BuNo 34991 of VPB-150, Tarawa, 1944–45

15
PV-1 BuNo 49418 flown by Crew 4, VPB-151, Tinian, Mariana Islands, 1944–45

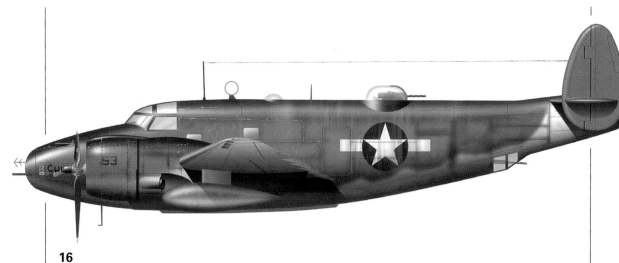

16
PV-1 BuNo 33253 flown by Capt J H Wehman, VMF(N)-531, Russell and Treasury Islands, South Pacific, February 1944

17
PV-1 2195 of No 149 Sqn, Prince Rupert, British Columbia, 1943

18
PV-1 NZ4503 (ex-BuNo 33309) of No 1 Sqn, Whenuapi, New Zealand, June 1943

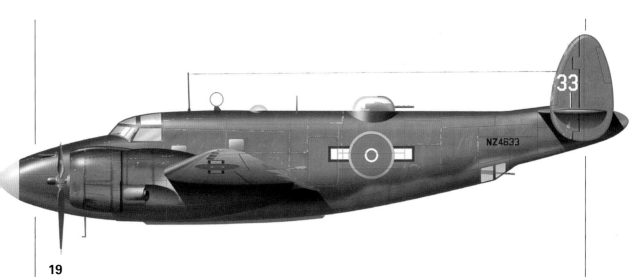

19
PV-1 NZ4633 (ex-BuNo 49579) of No 3 Sqn, Green Island, South Pacific, April 1945

20
PV-1 NZ4525 (ex-BuNo 34678) of No 2 Sqn, Henderson Field, Guadalcanal, September 1943

21
PV-1 'White 34' of No 1 Bombing Operational Training Unit, Ohakea, New Zealand, 1945

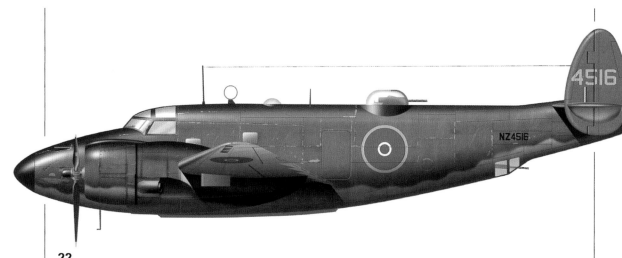

22
PV-1 NZ4516 (ex-BuNo 33440) flown by Flt Lt Spicer, No 1 Sqn, Henderson Field, Guadalcanal, December 1943

23
PV-1 A59-61 of No 13 Sqn, Gove, Northern Territory, 1944–45

24
Ventura Mk II AE939 of No 464 Sqn, Feltwell, December 1942

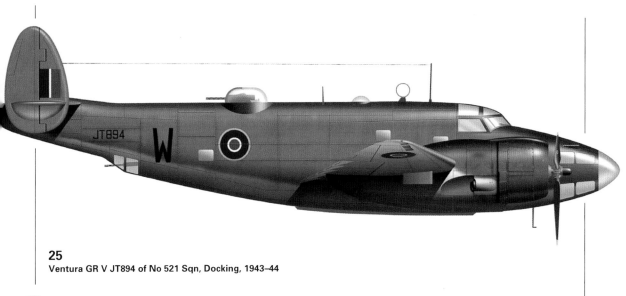

25
Ventura GR V JT894 of No 521 Sqn, Docking, 1943–44

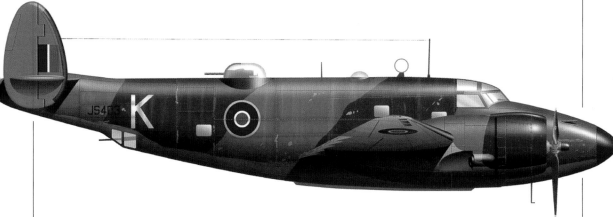

26
Ventura GR V JS403 of No 22 Sqn, Italy, June 1944

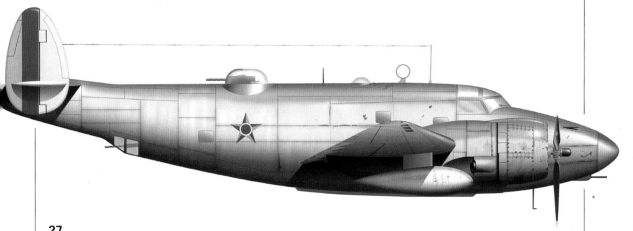

27
PV-1 of the *1° Grupo de Bombardeio Médio*, Recife, Brazil, 1945

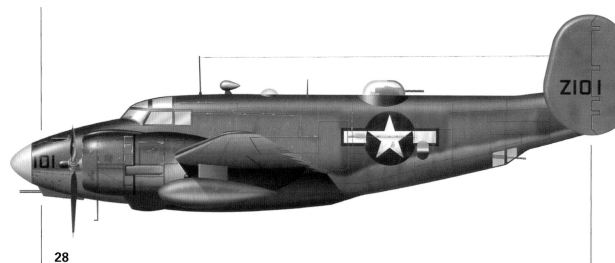

28
PV-2 BuNo 37101 of VPB-142/153, NAS Kaneohe, Hawaii, May 1945

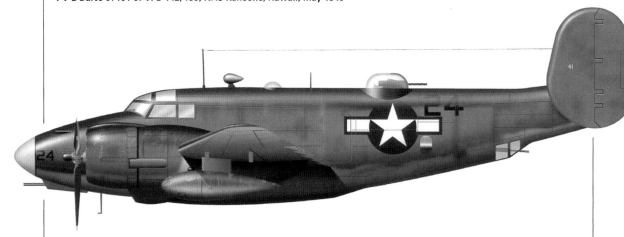

29
PV-2 'Black 24' (BuNo unknown) of VPB-139, flown by Lt Alfred 'Fritz' Daniel, Attu Island, Alaska, March 1945

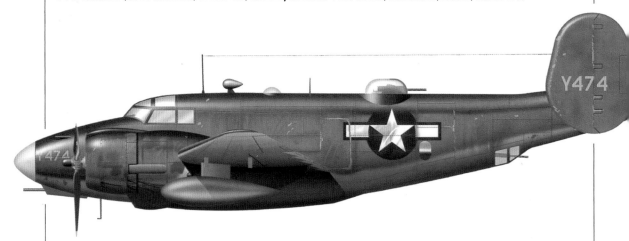

30
PV-2 BuNo 37474 of VPB-148, FAW-2, NAS Kaneohe, Hawaii, June 1945

mountainous, jungle-covered island. There were only 500 Japanese troops on Morotai when the American 31st Infantry Division landed on 15 September 1944. The defenders were rapidly reduced in number to 200, and once these men had fled into the jungle, engineers began work on an airfield at Wawama. This strip would soon play an important role in the upcoming invasion of the Philippines, as it was the nearest site from which long-range patrol aircraft could search north and west of Leyte.

For PV-1 crews, Morotai was remembered for its mud, mosquitoes, occasionally a python and frequently a Japanese infiltrator. Indeed, there was hardly a night that went by without a solitary enemy aircraft (nicknamed 'Washing-machine Charlie') overflying the base, dropping bombs. In addition, there were also air raids of significant size, which destroyed PV-1s on the ground. On one such occasion a Japanese bomber was shot down, and Capt C B 'Doc' Jones of FAW-17 remarked, 'That crew may have given their heart to the Emperor, but we got their ass!'

VB-146 was assigned search sectors in northern Borneo and the Sulu Archipelago, the areas over and east of Mindanao and the central and north Celebes. In addition to undertaking numerous patrols, the unit also flew strikes on the seaplane facility in Illigan Bay.

Lt Cdr Jesse P Robinson was on one such mission, covering a search sector that extended from the Celebes Sea to the Sulu Archipelago, when he decided to pay a visit to the enemy seaplane base on Sanga Sanga once he had come to the end of the search sector at Tawi Tawi. He was at the controls of the XO's PV-1 (BuNo 34800) on this occasion, as a member of the gas crew had accidently dropped a roll of Lifesaver sweets into the main fuel tank of his aircraft! Robinson recalls:

'I made a couple of strafing runs on the aircraft and a service boat. I then made a glide attack on the ramp and facilities. The 100-lb (45-kg) bombs did a proper number on the ramp and service area, as well as the aircraft on the beach.'

Fire from small calibre weapons was heavy, however, and the PV-1 suffered a hit to its left engine, cutting the hydraulic line and rendering the R2800 inoperable. Robinson headed back to Morotai, jettisoning his drop tanks and pulling open the escape hatch as he neared home.

His approach was made at 110 knots (126 mph or 203 km/h), keeping the left wing low. The aeroplane touched down on the runway and the left wing hit the ground and swung the aircraft through a 150-degree turn. Miraculously, none of the crew was injured, and the aeroplane was soon back in service.

In October 1944 VPB-146 was called upon to participate in what would have been the first torpedo strike conducted by Venturas. On the 24th, Commander Seventh Fleet ordered VPB-146 to stand by for a torpedo attack on the Japanese fleet as the battle of Leyte Gulf unfolded (23–26 October). The

The severed aft fuselage of PV-1 'Black 884' of VPB-146 lies off the side of the runway after crash-landing on Pyitlu Island, in the Admiralty Islands chains. Despite their aircraft being written off, the crew of this Ventura managed to escape unharmed
(*Dick Hendrickson via VMAF*)

PV-1s had their bomb-bay doors removed and torpedo racks installed. However, the following day these orders were rescinded.

In November VPB-137 arrived at Morotai for its second tour of duty in the Central Pacific. Between 3 and 10 December the unit conducted a series of four-aeroplane attacks on a radio station on Tobi and installations at Lalos. Enemy aircraft were still prevalent in this area at the time, and on 14 December Lt Irving A Enveold intercepted an F1M2 'Pete' floatplane off the south-western tip of Tawi Tawi Island and shot it down with his fixed nose guns.

RECOGNITION PROBLEMS

Poor recognition skills by allied fighter pilots seems to have plagued PV-1 units in the Pacific, as there are several reported instances of Venturas being damaged or shot down by US fighters. For example, on 26 November 1944, Lt Clifford Jackson of VPB-146 was flying PV-1 BuNo 34882 near Halmahera when he was attacked by two USAAF P-40s (flown by Lts Howell and Pittman) of the 82nd TRS.

The fighters each made one pass, destroying the Ventura's rudder and flap controls, puncturing a tyre and shattering the glass of the top turret. The gunner, R L Crutchfield, received a leg wound from a 0.50-cal bullet and almost bled to death before the aircraft was able to land. The P-40s were about to make a second run when Jackson was able to take cover in some heavy cumulus clouds. Realising they had just attacked a Navy aeroplane, the P-40s escorted the PV-1 home. Jackson arrived at Morotai and made a straight-in landing, but the left brake would not work and the right tyre soon came off. The gear duly collapsed and the PV-1 skidded along on its left wing before finally coming to a halt.

An overall view of VPB-146's Ventura 'Black 884'. Its nose cone has been removed following the crash, revealing the radar dish for the aircraft's ASD-1 surface search system (*via Dick Hendrickson via VMFA*)

Ventura 'Black 886' (BuNo 34886) served in the South Pacific as part of Lt Cdr Robinson's VPB-146. This aircraft survived its tour of duty and was then sent to a training unit. Very few PV-1s survived the wholesale post-war scrapping of military aircraft (*via Bill Scott*)

On 19 December P-47 Thunderbolts attacked a Ventura piloted by VPB-137's Lt Hancock. Three of the fighters began a firing pass, but two broke off before they were in range of the PV-1. The sole remaining P-47 did open fire, and the Ventura's turret gunner, fearing for the crew's safety, fired back. He shattered the fighter's canopy and wounded the pilot, who broke off his attack and returned to base. Hancock made it back to Morotai, but upon landing the port gear leg collapsed and the PV-1 screeched to a halt. The crew walked away with minor injuries.

On 1 December 1944 VPB-146 was replaced by VPB-130 and transferred back to the Admiralties, where it ran sector search into the Western Caroline Islands. In February 1945 the unit was ordered back to San Diego, via Hawaii, for reforming. During its tour of duty, VB/VPB-146 had lost 14 aircraft and three crews – one had been shot down and two failed to return from their patrols (both were lost on 20 October 1944).

Squadron member Max Hartman was very proud of the unit:

'In my mind VPB-146 is not a number but a group of men who lived closely together for many months. During this time, we endured both boredom and tragedy, as well as enjoying good times. We laughed at the bad times, and some of us matured while others died. Except for those who died, we did not do extraordinary or heroic things, but we all did what we were called upon to do.'

VENTURAS IN THE PHILIPPINES

As previously mentioned, VPB-146 was replaced in the front line by VPB-130, which had already completed a tour in the Caribbean with FAW-11. On 5 November 1944 the unit arrived at Tacloban, on Leyte, and thus became the first land-based bomber unit to operate from the Philippines. Indeed, VPB-130 had flown in just 15 days after the landings on Leyte. Located on the shore of San Pedro Bay, which separates the islands of Leyte and Samar, Tacloban had been captured by the US Army in late October, allowing engineers to begin work on creating an airfield.

Upon its arrival, VPB-130 had strict orders to avoid any contact with the enemy which might jeopardise the successful completion of its reconnaissance mission, and land targets could not be attacked under any circumstance. It did not say anything about attacking enemy aircraft, however!

On the afternoon of 11 November Lt Richard V Umphrey was on a routine search when he spotted a Japanese L2D 'Tabby' transport aeroplane 80 miles (128 km) south-east of Manila. He pulled alongside it and let his turret gunner open fire, then flew over it and had his ventral gunner let off a few bursts. Umphrey recalled, 'I thought my gunners needed the experience'. The pilot then flew ahead of the transport and came at it from head-on. Firing the nose guns, he knocked out the transport's starboard engine and riddled the fuselage. Coming back around for another pass, Umphrey latched onto the L2D's tail and shot it down in flames.

Three months later, on 12 February, Lt Umphrey and his crew failed to return from a routine patrol in PV-1 BuNo 49964.

From 27 December 1944 to 25 April 1945, VPB-130 conducted offensive searches from Pitoe airfield, on Morotai, flying four search sectors that covered Halmahera, the Celebes, western New Guinea, eastern Borneo, the Sulu Archipelago and southern Mindanao. In April,

VPB-130's tour of duty ended. Between 5 November 1944 and 25 April 1945, it had spotted 394 enemy vessels and damaged or destroyed 94 of them. Two enemy aircraft had also been shot down, three radar stations demolished and ground installations and equipment destroyed.

TACLOBAN

The next unit to arrive in the Philippines was VPB-137, which flew into Morotai on New Year's Day 1945 to commence its second tour. Two days after arriving, the squadron lost 11 of its PV-1s in a Japanese air raid, and replacements had to be flown in by VPB-128.

Between March and May VPB-137 was split between Clark Field and Tacloban. The unit conducted bombing strikes almost daily during the period, and interception by Japanese fighters occurred on occasion. On 1 March, VPB-149, commanded by Lt Cdr Milton W Swan, joined VPB-137 on Tacloban, and began combat patrols to northern Borneo, Palawan and eastern Luzon. Lt Cdr Swan's unit was the last Navy PV-1 squadron to arrive in the Philippines before the end of hostilities. During the months to come, VPB-137 and -149 would be given the task of 'mopping up' pockets of Japanese resistance in the area.

On 12 March, VPB-149 lost two aircraft and one crew when Lt E A Brigham was forced to ditch BuNo 49612 at sea after getting lost in bad weather and Lt J J Boyd's machine (BuNo 49631) crashed near Leyte. Between 20 and 27 March, VPB-149 attacked Japanese troop concentrations in the Negros area, inflicting considerable casualties. On one such strike, Lt Cdr Charles M Wood Jr and his crew failed to return from an attack on Pontevedra Village.

On 10 May VPB-137 staged its first attack on the butanol refineries at Mato and Shoka, on Formosa. These targets would be routinely visited over the coming weeks, as would Japanese troop concentrations in upper Cagayan Valley and railroad facilities on Formosa.

The versatility of the PV-1, and its ability to fly at speeds that nearly matched enemy fighters, was clearly demonstrated during this period when Lt(jg) Joe B Locker attacked a pair of Ki-43 'Oscars' ten miles (16 km) south-east of Amoy, in China, and sent one down in flames.

THE TWO-OCEAN RAIDERS – VPB-128

After a tour of duty in the Atlantic, where the unit enjoyed some success hunting German submarines, VPB-128 arrived in the Pacific theatre in the autumn of 1944. Under the command of Lt Cdr Jay B Yakeley Jr, the squadron trained in Pacific Fleet doctrines of anti-submarine warfare, fighter affiliation, night and day torpedo and formation tactics, radar and low-level bombing.

By 13 October VPB-128 was based at Hawaii, with half the unit operating from Midway. It was whilst flying from the latter base that Lt Stanley Miller achieved what engineers said was impossible in a PV-1. When taking off from Midway, one of his engines failed completely, and in the excitement of keeping the aeroplane right side up and in the air, Miller and his co-pilot neglected to jettison bombs, drop tanks or lose gear. Design studies indicated that a PV-1 could not fly on one engine when carrying such a load, but Miller circled the strip at very low altitude and landed back on the runway without inflicting any damage to the bomber.

From 29 December 1944 to 27 February 1945, the unit was stationed at Owi Island, in the Netherlands East Indies. Operationally, VPB-128's wings were temporarily clipped when 11 of VPB-137's 14 PV-1s were destroyed in a bombing raid on the night of 3 January. Within 48 hours 12 of VPB-128's Venturas had been flown to Tacloban to make good VPB-137's losses, and it was not until 1 March, when the unit arrived at Guiuan, in Samar, that it could devote itself to anti-submarine

searches and convoy coverage. According to Harold M Forrest, a PV-1 aeroplane commander with VPB-128, 'The replacement aircraft were a group of tired PVs from FAW-2. They were certainly a far cry from the new aeroplanes we had brought out from the States'.

On 18 March three PV-1s, flown by Lts Joseph F Dorrington, Frederick W Snyder and Henry T James, spotted two enemy midget submarines in Davao Gulf and attacked them, achieving one kill and a probable.

On 18 and 22 March 1945 VPB-128 sank two midget submarines. This particular example, fitted with a flotation device, was discovered off Davao, in the Philippines. It was attacked moments after this photograph was taken (*via NARA*)

Three days later, another three-aeroplane division attacked a midget submarine tied up to a wharf in Cebu City. Damaging the submarine with rockets, VPB-128 despatched five more PV-1s the next day in order to finish the vessel off. Leading them was Lt Cdr William Tepuni, the unit's executive officer, who made a successful bombing attack. However, his aircraft (BuNo 34888) was hit by anti-aircraft fire and it crashed, killing all on board. A few seconds later Lt George A Hall made a

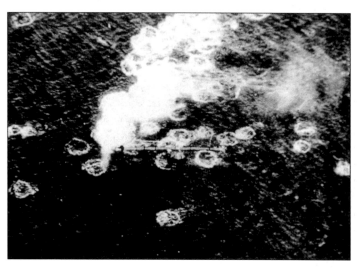

second bombing run and completed the destruction of the submarine with three direct hits.

Lt Cdr Tepuni was greatly respected by all members of the unit, and in a squadron report issued after his death, he was viewed as a man who, 'firmly believed that the success of a military mission is based on dedication to duty, extensive training and practice, practice, practice. He was noted as one who never gave an order to officers or enlisted men that he would not perform himself.'

Within minutes the midget submarine had been struck by a hail of machine gun bullets and a rocket projectile, fired from the VPB-128 PV-1. Such an attack led to the death of the unit's XO, Lt Cdr William Tepuni, on 22 March 1945 (*via NARA*)

PALAWAN

On 5 April VPB-128 departed Tacloban for Palawan Island, the fifth largest land mass in the Philippine archipelago. Lying between the China and Sulu Seas, it extends some 270 miles (434 km) north-east to south-west, reaching a maximum width of just 24 miles (38 km). Gen Douglas MacArthur wanted Palawan as a base to extend air power to the South China Sea and the Dutch East Indies, and on 28 February 1945 the 41st Division's 186th Regimental Combat Team went ashore and secured the island. So crucial was the airstrip on this island that even before Palawan had been totally seized from Japanese control, Navy patrol squadrons had begun flying out of Westbrook Field.

The island's 5000-ft (1524-m) runway – part Marston mat, part unrolled coral – was extremely narrow, being not more than 100 ft (30 m) wide, and it did not stand up under the constant traffic of USAAF B-24s, B-25s and P-38s. The airfield itself had been built by American PoWs. When it was nearly completed, the Japanese herded over 100 of them into an air raid shelter, poured gasoline on them and then set fire to them. Any prisoners who attempted to escape the inferno were shot. Now the airfield was in Allied hands.

With only one entrance to the taxi lane from the strip, all landings were made down wind to alleviate having to taxi back the full length of the runway. The field was closed from sunset to sunrise, and late-returning aeroplanes landed only with special permission, and after considerable delay.

On 28 April VPB-128 began flying missions against enemy supply lines and storage depots in northern Burma. Crews adapted to the new role with eagerness. Operating under the control of XIII Fighter Command, each PV-1 carried two 1000-lb napalm bombs, three 250-lb general-purpose bombs and eight 5-in HVAR rockets. During this phase of the conflict, Brig Gen E W Barnes, commanding officer of XIII Fighter Command, commended the unit, telling them that, 'The spirit and performance displayed by you and your unit merit special credit to you and the members of your command'.

While operations against enemy targets continued, Westbrook Field became the target of token bombing raids by Japanese aircraft flying out of Sandakan airstrip in Borneo. Damage from the attacks was negligible, but it did interfere with the sleep of personnel stationed at the airfield.

On 28 May two Navy PB4Y-2 Privateers from VPB-106, two PB4Y-1 Liberators from VPB-111 and six PV-1 Venturas from VPB-128 attacked Sandakan. Carrying four 1000-lb (453-kg) bombs apiece, the four PB4Ys hit the airfield from a height of just 600 ft (182 m), while the Venturas went in even lower, bombing and strafing. There was not much left of Sandakan by the time they had finished, and the Japanese never bombed Palawan again.

With the elimination of the the nocturnal threat, PV-1 crews began to enjoy uninterrupted sleep, which was a crucial escape from the rigors of combat. In June 1945, with the campaign in Borneo winding down, VPB-128 was transferred to

Aircrew and native workers attempt to dry out their belongings in front of the living quarters for VPB-151 personnel on Tinian in early 1945. Pacific PV-1 squadrons were often accommodated in tents such as these, which barely kept out the rain (*via Daryl Hahn*)

Tinian, in the Mariana Islands. For the remainder of the war, it would fly 'whitecap' patrols.

THE GREY GHOSTS

By the end of 1942, and with American forces entrenched on Guadalcanal, the Japanese switched from day to night bombing raids. This lowered the combat efficiency of US ground troops through loss of sleep, as men had to spend hours in foxholes and air raid shelters. Therefore, theatre commander Adm William Halsey requested that a unit specially equipped for nightfighting be formed and sent to the Solomon Islands. This was not an easy task to fulfil, as radar-equipped American aircraft, at that time, existed only on paper.

The need for such a machine was not new, as US military officers had been sent to Great Britain in 1941 to learn about RAF nightfighter operations. Among them was Marine Corps Maj Frank H Schwable. When he returned to Washington, he brought with him operating information for the British Mk IV radar.

On 16 November 1942 the first Marine nightfighter unit, designated as VMF(N)-531, was authorised, with Maj Schwable as commanding officer and Maj John D Harshberger as executive officer. Establishing a squadron was one thing, but finding a suitable aircraft was another. Indeed, the types available to Schwable were limited.

The preferred aircraft were the Navy's F4U Corsair and the USAAF's P-61 Black Widow. However, the former would not be ready until January 1943, and the P-61 not until June. In a Bureau of Aeronautics conference held on 2 July 1942, Schwable was told that a few B-34 Venturas were available in a 'pinch'. With nothing else on offer, VMF(N)-531 received Venturas just prior to Christmas 1942.

The bombers were modified through the fitment of Mk IV radar, IFF (Identification Friend or Foe) equipment and VHF radar at NAS Quonset Point, Rhode Island, while additional nose-firing 0.50-cal guns, oxygen equipment and gunsights were installed at NAS Norfolk, Virginia.

For the next six months, Schwable and Hearshberger were under constant pressure to get the unit fit for service overseas. However, VMF(N)-531 was plagued by a shortage of spare parts for the radar, suitable test equipment, effective radios and, on occasion, aeroplanes. Moreover, the nose guns malfunctioned and the aircraft were not allowed to fly above 15,000 ft (4572 m) because of a faulty oxygen system. Schwable officially recorded his dislike for the Ventura in a memorandum, dated 28 May 1943:

'If it is the desire of the Bureau (Navy Bureau of Aeronautics) to have this unit proceed to the combat zone in an aeroplane that is admittedly makeshift for the job, with guns that may or may not fire, instruments that are difficult to read and with radar that so far has an average of one out of three working, this unit will plan accordingly and accept, without comment, the experimental installations furnished.'

With his dissatisfaction noted, Schwable, six PV-1s and 30 men of VMF(N)-531 were loaded aboard the USS *Long Island* (CVE-1) at NAS North Island, in San Diego, on 1 August 1943 and sent to Pearl Harbor. By 25 August the unit had arrived at Espiritu Santo, and a few days later Schwable and Harshberger flew to Banika, in the Russell Islands.

On 11 September, five PV-1s and their aircrews, along with 16 ground-crew, were brought up from Noumea, in New Caledonia.

NIGHT OPERATIONS

Nightfighting was a complicated undertaking which involved not only the aircraft and crew, but a ground controller (Ground Control Intercept (GCI), using a mobile SCR-527A radar) whose task it was to guide the aeroplane to the interception point, where the PV-1's radar operator took over locating the 'bogey' (enemy aircraft).

The first two months of operations for VMF(N)-531 saw aircraft lost and no enemy contacts made. The first fatalities were suffered on 16 September when Lt John E Mason, with radar operator S/Sgt R W Emerson and gunner Cpl J J Burkett, went on a practice flight in PV-1 BuNo 29755 to test the GCI and simply disappeared. During the first month of operations there were six scrambles against enemy aircraft, but they were unsuccessful mainly due to the inexperience of the ground controllers.

In late September, three PV-1s were moved to Munda, on New Georgia Island, where numerous radar contacts with enemy aircraft were made, but none were intercepted. From 14 September to 27 October, VMF(N)-531 flew 47 night combat missions, including eight scrambles, and attempted to close on 17 'bogies' without any luck.

As landings on Bougainville neared, the unit was ordered to fly night Combat Air Patrols over the landing ships. On the night of 13–14 November, Capt Duane R Jenkins was directed towards a single 'bogey'.

The contact was some 4000 ft (1219 m) away from the PV-1 according to the radar, heading from right to left. A moment later the 'bogey', identified as a G4M 'Betty', came into sight at a distance of just 1500 ft (457 m), Capt Jenkins spotting its exhaust flames. Closing to within 800 ft (234 m), he gave the bomber a four-second burst and the 'Betty's' starboard engine nacelle was set alight. The aircraft then went into a shallow dive, and Jenkins caught it again with a short burst into the port wing root. He fired a third burst and the turret gunner also let fly with a two-second burst into the fuselage. The Japanese bomber went into a steep dive and exploded upon hitting the water.

During the Bougainville campaign, there was considerable discussion about the value of using nightfighters. Many allied commanders wanted the fighters pulled away from enemy aircraft as they approached anti-aircraft positions because it was felt that flak was a more effective deterrent. Secondly, the sight and sound of anti-aircraft gun being fired was considered a morale booster for the embattled troops on the ground. Col Schwable devoted considerable time dispelling such thoughts and, in the end, the use of nightfighters would be justified.

On 1 December VMF(N)-531 was reinforced by the arrival of three additional Venturas and crews. However, two nights later the unit lost another aircraft and crew when Capt Jenkins took off to cover a task group and destroyer squadron being attacked by an estimated 15 to 25 enemy aircraft. Jenkins was seen to shoot down another machine, but his PV-1 (BuNo 29857) failed to return to base. Killed along with Jenkins were T/Sgt Charles H Stout and Sgt T J Glennon.

Jenkins' death did not subdue the will of the unit to take out enemy aircraft, and three nights later another Japanese aircraft fell to the guns of

CHLOE **was an early model PV-1 used by VMF(N)-531 in January 1944. The Marine Corps modified the PV-1 into a nightfighter through the fitment of AI Mk IV air-search radar and extra nose guns, and then used it in the South Pacific. The antenna for the AI radar can just be seen protruding from the nose of this machine (***NARA***)**

a VMF(N)-531 PV-1. Maj Harshberger's radar operator T/Sgt J S Kinne had spotted a 'bogey' on his scope just after midnight. Harshberger slowed to 130 knots (140 mph or 240 km/h), and had closed to within 2500 ft (762 m) of the contact when he saw an E13A 'Jake' floatplane silhouetted in the moonlight.

At 800 ft (243 m), he and turret gunner S/Sgt Walter E Tiedeman fired bursts from slightly below the enemy aircraft. Almost immediately the 'Jake' fell away to the right in flames, before crashing into the water.

When not engaged as nightfighters, VMF(N)-531's Venturas were used to attack Japanese installations and ships in an attempt to cut off supplies reaching troops on Bougainville. The most common form of transport employed by the enemy was the barge, and these usually moved under the cover of darkness.

On 11 December Col Schwable dropped two 100-lb (45-kg) bombs on a dock and ramp area on the western shore of Faisi, and watched as a large explosion, followed by a series of secondary explosions, covered half the island in flames. Photos taken the following day revealed a burnt out area measuring 200 sq ft (18 sq m) which was believed to have been a fuel dump. Despite missions like this one adding significantly to the harassment of the enemy, Col Schwable remained adamant that 'nightfighting is the principal business of the PV-1'. XO Harshberger, on the other hand, 'enjoyed fighting my own little war with night bombing'.

On 9 January 1944 the squadron moved to Piva airfield, on Bougainville. Three days later Schwable was flying a patrol from the base with his regular crew, radar operator S/Sgt Robert I Ward and gunner Sgt William J Fletcher, when they made two contacts. As Schwable tried to close in on the second 'bogey', Fletcher sighted a B5N 'Kate' some 3000 ft (914 m) away. Closing to 500 ft (152 m), Schwable and Fletcher fired at it simultaneously, and 'immediately the aeroplane exploded and burst into flames'.

In order to avoid the wreckage, the pilot swung hard left and felt scorching heat as his right wing just cleared the flaming debris. The 'Kate' exploded again just before it hit the water. Schwable reported, 'The action had taken just nine minutes from start to finish'.

MORE KILLS

January 1944 saw several operational developments. The unit's radar intercept section was moved from Vella Lavella to the Treasury Islands, where it could better cover some of the shipping routes. In addition, the third, and last, echelon of five PV-ls and six pilots arrived from the US. VMF(N)-531 was now set to counter Japanese air attacks in the region, which would reach their peak the following month.

Battles with enemy aeroplanes began on the night of 5–6 February when Schwable and his crew took off from Piva and were vectored by an Army controller onto a 'bogey' cruising at an altitude of 15,000 ft (4572 m). As the PV-1 climbed up to meet it, S/Sgt Ward was able to make radar contact at a distance of 12,000 ft (3657 m), but the PV-1 had to close to within 700 ft (213 m) before Schwable could identify it as a G4M 'Betty'. He and Fletcher opened fire, hitting the bomber's fuselage. The 'Betty' turned to starboard in an attempt to escape, only to be hit by another burst from the PV-1. It spiralled into the water and exploded.

Three days later VMF(N)-531 suffered another operational loss when, on the night of 9–10 February, 1Lt Clifford W Watson and his crew (Sgt J H Shirk and gunner Sgt O E Brogna) took off in bad weather in Ventura BuNo 33253 and crashed into the water just minutes later. The fuelled-up PV-1 burst into flames, killing all three men.

Later that night Harshberger's radar operator T/Sgt Kinne made contact with a 'bogey' at a range of 12,000 ft (3657 m). Climbing to 15,000 ft (4572 m), which was the maximum ceiling for the PV-1, the crew closed to within 4000 ft (1219 m) of the contact when the radar blip split into two. At a distance of 2500 ft (762 m), turret gunner T/Sgt Tiedeman identified the two 'bogies' as G4M 'Betty' bombers. As Harshberger closed to within 2000 ft (609m), both Japanese aircraft began firing their 20 mm tail cannon.

Harshberger targeted the 'Betty' to the left and opened fire with his six nose guns. At this point the PV-1 was itself hit in the nose, putting five of the six guns out of commission. However, Harshberger continued to fire with the remaining weapon. While the Ventura pilot dealt with one 'Betty', T/Sgt Tiedeman fired a burst into the tail gunner of the G4M on the right, which then peeled off out of range. He then swung his turret back in the direction of the bomber to the left, and fired three bursts into it. The 'Betty' went into a steep nose-dive and crashed. With his fuel nearly gone, and his radio knocked out, Harshberger turned for home.

Approaching the airfield, searchlights went on, followed by 'friendly' flak directed towards the Ventura. Harshberger, however, managed to land safely, and later stated, 'I never had so much fun in my life!'

On the night of 14–15 February, whilst covering the invasion of Green Island, VMF(N)-531 flew eight Combat Air Patrols. On Schwable's second patrol of the night, while covering the amphibious force that was scheduled to invade at dawn, Sgt Ward spotted a 'bogey' at a distance of 2000 ft (609 m). It was an E13A 'Jake' floatplane, and when the PV-1 had closed to within 700 ft (213 m), Schwable opened fire. The 'Jake's' engine caught fire and it dramatically slowed, causing the PV-1 to fly by so close that Sgt Fletcher later stated that he could have hit the pilot over the head with his gun butt! Destroyer crews covering the amphibious landing force watched as the flaming 'Jake' hit the water.

The invading force of Australian and New Zealand troops encountered little ground opposition when they went ashore on the 15th. The island, and its atolls, proved to be a worthwhile acquisition, for it boasted an airstrip situated just 220 miles (354 km) from Kavieng, 115 miles (185 km) from Rabaul and 720 miles (1158 km) from Truk. The largest of the atolls in the Green Island chain was Nissan, which was some eight miles (13 km) long. It duly became a base for allied air operations, despite being hot, humid and muddy. There was also no fresh water, except for what could be caught when it rained . . . and it rained frequently.

Immediately after Green Island fell, VMF(N)-531 established a radar site in the area and commenced patrols. On the night of 16–17 February, ground control located a 'bogey' and vectored Schwable in for the kill. S/Sgt Ward acquired the target on his screen at a range of 5000 ft (1524 m), and the enemy aircraft was spotted visually at 2000 ft (609 m). It was yet another E13A 'Jake'.

Closing to within 300 ft (91 m), Schwable fired his nose guns and Sgt Fletcher opened up with his turret guns. The 'Jake' literally disintegrated under the weight of fire, its wings folding up. Frank Schwable was credited with his fourth, and last, kill, making him the leading nightfighter pilot in the Pacific at that time. This would also prove to be his final flight, for he handed over command of VMF(N)-531 to Lt Col Harshberger.

1Lt Jack M Plunkett also flew a patrol later that night, along with his radar operator S/Sgt Floyd M Pulham and and gunner S/Sgt Michael J Cipkala. Green Island radar vectored him onto a 'bogey' and Pulham made radar contact at 4000 ft (1219 m). At 400 ft (121 m) Plunkett spotted an E13A 'Jake' making violent S-turns, and he fired several bursts at the gyrating floatplane from a distance of 350 ft (106 m). It nosed down into a vertical dive and burst into flames upon hitting the water.

On 19 February Harshberger was vectored onto a 'bogey' (yet another 'Jake'), and his radar operator, T/Sgt Kinne, made contact. The pilot closed to within 300 ft (91 m) and fired. The fuselage of the floatplane burst into flames and dropped away in a steep vertical dive into the water, where it burned fiercely.

Landing back at Bougainville, Harshberger's elation was tempered by a report that 1Lt Thaddeus M Banks and his crew, S/Sgts B C Bowers and G Jones, had not returned (in PV-1 BuNo 33089) from a barge search and strafing mission. Harshberger immediately took off on a fruitless five-hour search. The next day, another aeroplane spotted a PV-1 wheel, cabin tank and parachute floating in the sea.

By the end of February 1944, Rabaul's air power had been reduced to just six aircraft, and VMF(N)-531 suddenly found itself without any targets. Harshberger complained:

'This squadron is hoping to be moved to some area where there will be more business. They (Japanese) seem to get the word when nightfighters move into an area, and they stay away at night.'

WINDING DOWN

Operations continued into March, with strafing and bombing attacks being the primary focus of VMF(N)-531's activities. On 3 March, Harshberger found five barges, which Sgt Kinne illuminated with flares to allow the pilot to strafe them. Three were duly sunk.

Ten days later Harshberger and his crew engaged one of the few surviving Japanese aircraft in the area. Forty-five minutes after take-off, a contact was made at a range of 8000 ft over Empress Augusta Bay. Closing to 1500 ft (457 m), the pilot spotted an E16A1 'Paul' – the first such sighting of this new Aichi floatplane, which was being operated by No 14 Experimental Reconnaissance Squadron. Firing his guns from 300 ft (91 m), Harshberger quickly sent the aircraft down in flames.

On 21 March, the unit suffered a double blow when PV-1s BuNos 29870 and 33079 collided in mid-air. Lt Marvin E Notestine and his crew had taken off at 0520 hrs and patrolled until 0630 hrs, when the PV-1 headed for home. Two aircraft, flown by Lts Pierce and Birdsall,

Some of the officers of VMF(N)-531 stand in front of an SNJ Texan trainer on 12 December 1942. They are, from left to right, Capt Rose Mickey, Capt Raymond George, Maj Edward Hodgson, Lt Col Frank Schwable (Commanding Officer), Maj John Harshberger (Executive Officer), Capt William Kellum and 1Lt Duane Jenkins. Fellow squadron pilots Capts Peter Lambrecht and Homer Hutchinson were still in England at the time, flying RAF Beaufighters (*via Hill Goodspeed*)

joined him, and they flew in formation towards Vella Lavella. At about 0650 hrs, Lt Pierce's wing clipped Lt Birdsall's, causing Pierce's aeroplane to burst into flames and Birdsall's PV-1 to enter an irrecoverable spin. Lt Notestine barely avoided colliding with Pierce's flaming Ventura as both PV-1s crashed into the sea, killing all nine men on board the two aircraft.

VMF(N)-531 made no hostile contacts in April, and on 6 May Col Harshberger handed the unit over to Capt Wehmer and headed back to the US with seven of his pilots, three ground officers, 68 men and all but three of the radar controllers.

On 11 May 1Lt Notestine and his crew (Sgt E H Benintende and Cpl W M Kinn) made contact with a 'bogey' while over the St George Channel. Notestine saw an E13A 'Jake' pass in the opposite direction some 200 ft (60 m) below him, so he turned his PV-1 around and chased the floatplane into the naval base anchorage at Rabaul's Simpson Harbour. The 'Jake' was preparing to land when Notestine fired a burst at a range of 400 ft (121 m), causing the floatplane to burst into flames and hit the water. He had scored the unit's 12th, and final, victory.

At the conclusion of VMF(N)-531's tour, ComAirSols Brig Gen Earl W Barnes praised the unit's record, noting that the dramatic reduction in enemy night air activity 'has been largely due to the successful efforts of VMF(N)-531, operating with antiquated equipment and an abundance of personal effort and ability of all members of the organisation'.

Despite claiming four kills, Col Schwable, in his historical summary of VMF(N)-531, made clear his distaste for the PV-1 as a nightfighter:

'The PV-1 aeroplane has been entirely unsatisfactory as a nightfighter due to its low performance and other deficiencies. It is recognised that the PV-1 was the only twin-engined aircraft available for nightfighter work at the time VMF(N)-531 was organised, and that single-engined aircraft were later converted to use as nightfighters for the same reason.

'All Marine Corps pilots who observed and trained with nightfighting units in England expressed the opinion that single-engined aircraft would never be entirely satisfactory as nightfighters. They strongly recommended that a suitable twin-engined type be adopted. The operations of nightfighter aircraft in this area have borne out this contention, and it is believed that no single-engined aircraft will ever be as satisfactory, or give as good results, as a twin-engined aeroplane designed for this role.'

OPERATIONS IN THE CENTRAL PACIFIC

While the allies slogged their way through the tropical islands of the South Pacific towards their ultimate goal of liberating the Philippines, naval planners shifted their focus to the island chains of the Central Pacific. The generally flat terrain and abundance of coral on the islands made them suitable for the construction of airstrips, while the lagoons afforded natural harbours for shipping.

The Allies realised that the establishment of bases in the area would provide a stepping stone for future advances in the Philippines or Formosa, and that the islands would also eventually serve as bases for American naval and air power tasked with attacking the Japanese mainland.

In the autumn of 1943, Air Force Central Pacific was established under the leadership of Adm John Hoover. His command, at first, covered bases on the Ellice, Fijian and Samoan Islands. It was set up as a mobile unit, capable of moving westward through the Central Pacific as American forces gained control of Japanese strongholds in the region. Ultimately, it would include the Gilbert, Marshall, Mariana, Palau, Bonin and Volcano Islands (the latter including Iwo Jima).

The function of Commander Air Force Central Pacific was generally twofold. Hoover controlled both the land-based aircraft in the Central Pacific and the occupying forces which garrisoned the islands in the area. On 1 May 1944, the command title was changed to Forward Area, and on 1 June 1945 it was retitled Marianas Area. Its task force number was 57, although this became 94 on 20 November 1944.

THE FIRST

The first PV-1 unit to serve in the South Pacific was VB-137, which was commissioned on 17 February 1943 at NAS Alameda, California. In May–June 1943, the squadron ran separate detachments from Midway and Wallis, in the Ellice Islands, but by July the entire unit had been consolidated at the latter base so that it could fly search sectors around the Ellice Islands.

Very little offensive action was conducted at this stage, although in September VB-137 still managed to lose two aircraft and crews. On the 7th a PV-1 piloted by Lt Loyd E Parker failed to return from a routine search, and then 48 hours later Lt Leland L Nunn and his crew were also lost.

Officers of VB-137 are seen aboard the USS *Copahee* (CVE-12) on 14 May 1943, en route to the Pacific. In the middle row, sixth from left, is the squadron CO, Lt Cdr Eddie R Sanders. VB-137 initially served in the Central Pacific, before completing a second tour in the Philippines (*via NARA*)

PV-1 BuNo 49575 was serving with VB-137 when this photograph was taken at Morotai. The aircraft has the last three digits of its BuNo painted both on its nose and tail fins (*Queensland Air Museum via VMAF*)

During the invasion of the Gilbert Islands in November 1943, the unit conducted low-level reconnaissance sorties for the American task force.

PV-1s IN THE GILBERTS

In December, VB-137 moved up to Betio, in the Gilbert Islands, just a week after it had fallen to US Marines. Conducting ASW sweeps in conjunction with Navy Liberator squadrons VB-108 and -109, the patrolling PV-1s failed to spot a single enemy vessel, and on 15 January 1944 the unit was relieved.

In mid-December 1943, Lt Cdr Clayton L Miller arrived in-theatre at Hawkins Field, on Tarawa, with VB-142. The unit had been operating PV-1s from Midway and Johnston Islands since August, after which it had performed the long-range scouting role from Wake Island. It had also attempted to intercept enemy submarines, but VB-142's overall score for this period was one confirmed kill on a whale, using three depth charges.

Living in tents, eating Spam and beans, smelling the stench of rotting Japanese corpses baking in the sun and fighting dysentery was the life led by the men from VB-142 at Hawkins Field. In the months to come they would fly 302 bombing sorties against Japanese forces in the Marshall Islands, losing one Ventura and its crew during the deployment.

This loss occurred on 12 January 1944 when 12 PV-1s were sortied to bomb and strafe Jabor township on Jaluat Atoll. The standard tactic of flying at 280 knots (322 mph or 518 km/h) at a height of just 50 ft (15 m) was employed as the unit approached the target. Making landfall at Jaluit, heavy anti-aircraft fire hit Lt M E Villa's bomber, which disintegrated when it hit the sea doing 280 knots. There were no survivors.

From then on squadron doctrine changed so that a glide-bombing approach was made at all targets from a height of 4500 ft (1371 m). The pilot would perform a 45-degree dive, then pull out at 2000 ft (609 m) as his bombs were released. Such tactics, although unsuccessful against moving ships, proved more effective when attacking ground installations.

VB-144

Next to arrive in-theatre was VB-144, which left America on 23 October 1943 and commenced operations from Midway on 5 November. Eight aeroplanes were kept on Midway for routine searches, and the remaining PV-1s were stationed at Johnston Island. During this period the unit patrolled three 500-mile, 13-degree, search sectors without success.

The first detachment of PV-1s from VB-144 reached Tarawa on 12 January 1944, and five 500-mile searches were flown the following day. Standard operational procedure at this time typically saw VB-142 and VB-144 conducting the searches on alternate days. However, this routine varied considerably when US forces began to soften up the Marshall Islands in preparation for the invasion of Kwajalein and Eniwetok Atoll. Both units duly conducted bombing raids on enemy strong points at Mille, Maloelap, Wotje, Jaluit (Marshall Islands) and Nauru.

Initially, damage inflicted on the PV-1s by anti-aircraft fire was negligible, but as more attacks were made at lower altitudes, so aircraft vulnerability to small arms fire increased.

On 19 January, a VB-144 crew led by Lt D M McAusland sighted two enemy ships in the lagoon of Ailingalapalap Atoll (Marshall Islands) and they immediately attacked from a height of 200 ft (60 m). Two 500-lb (227-kg) bombs were dropped, and they fell between the ships, which were anchored 100 ft (30 m) apart. During the encounter, the Ventura had been opposed by light and medium flak, but it had returned safely to base. The next day two PV-1s were sent back to finish off the damaged vessels, but they discovered that both ships had been run aground in an effort to save their cargo.

VB-144 would not leave the ships alone, however, and the following day a solitary aeroplane was sent to attack them. Two runs were made, a 500-lb bomb dropped and strafing was conducted from a height of just 40 ft (12 m). The unit sent out two more aircraft on the 22nd, with each PV-1 carrying four 500-lb and two 100-lb bombs. A glide-bombing attack was carried out, with approaches made at 4000 ft (1219 m). At approximately one mile out, each pilot put his aeroplane into a 40–60 degree glide, releasing the bombs at 1500 ft (457 m). These attacks resulted in more near misses.

The complete destruction of the ships occurred on the fourth day of attacks, when two more PV-1s were sent out, each carrying four 500-lb and eight 100-lb bombs. Low-level approaches were made and bombs released at 100 ft (30 m). Direct hits were observed on both ships with the 100-lb bombs, and the vessels were left burning.

OPERATIONS FROM THE MARSHALLS

The invasion of the Marshall Islands commenced on 1 February 1944 with Marine landings on Kwajalein. The doomed Japanese garrison of some 8000 men must have been horrified to see 12 aircraft carriers and eight battleships cruising off the coast. Within a few days only a handful of soldiers remained alive.

VB-144 conducted night attacks against Japanese installations on by-passed islands during the invasion. On one such mission against Wotje Atoll on 16 April, Lt Samuel C Peterson encountered a particularly troublesome machine gun position. He decided to neutralise the battery on his next patrol, and two days later an attack was made at tree-top level. The PV-1 crew were in for a surprise, as there were now two machine gun positions! Peterson's co-pilot, Lt(jg) K C McNatt, recalls the mission:

'As we pulled up to make a second strafing run, we noticed the port oil gauge dropping fast. There was no doubt, what had happened. The Japs had hit an oil line. Pete immediately hit the "red button" for the left engine, which feathered the prop. We had no problem on one engine without a bomb load. Matter of fact, as I remember, we climbed to about 500 ft (152 m) on the way back to Roi-Namur.'

Three days later Lt Peterson was killed instantly when he was struck by a small calibre explosive shell during yet another low-level attack on Wotje Atoll. Lt(jg) McNatt took control of the aeroplane when it was just 50 ft (15 m) above the target, and he went on to land it safely at Kwajalein, despite damage to the controls . . . and the fact that he had never landed a PV-1 before. He remembers:

'As was normal for VB-144 in this type of procedure, we started on our target run from 5000 to 6000 ft, flying in a steep descent and erratic pattern as evasive action against ground anti-aircraft fire.

'Lt Peterson straightened the aeroplane at low level and high speed, and then began firing the bow guns. He also had the bomb-bay doors open in preparation for the bombing and strafing run. At the same time we spotted a Navy SBD Dauntless dive-bomber diving directly at the same target from the opposite direction. To avoid a collision with the SBD, or destruction by its bombs, Pete turned away from the air base target and circled in an anti-clockwise direction. Already at a height of about 100 ft, we lost excess speed by performing this manoeuvre.

'Having lost an engine over the same target just three days earlier, I frantically attempted to dissuade Pete from completing the run, but failed. Just before the bombs were to be released there was an explosion in the cockpit. Lt Peterson threw up his arms and glanced at me as if to say "take over" and then slumped forward.

'The shell that killed Peterson entered through the aeroplane's nose and exploded when it hit the pilot's control column in the cockpit, shattering the wheel drive chain and showering metal fragments throughout the aircraft.

'I grabbed the co-pilot's control column, applied full throttle and climbed for a safer altitude. As I glanced at Aeroplane Captain John Alderson, bare-chested and standing behind my co-pilot's seat, he was pointing at a small hole in his chest. He later learned that a piece of flak had ripped a hole several inches in diameter in his back as it exited his torso. At the same time, I could see that radioman C C Colgrove was wounded in his right shoulder. Although in great pain, and bleeding badly, Colgrove calmed down after Cpl Arthur Brandt (a Marine photographer) improvised a tourniquet – this probably saved his life.

'Tom Reed (Machinist Mate) and Larry Fitzgerald (Machinist Mate/Turret Gunner) removed Lt Peterson from the pilot's seat and made him as comfortable as possible on the deck aft of the radio compartment. However, Pete died in a few minutes. He had received the main force of the explosion, ripping open his mid-section and splattering blood and body tissue throughout the cockpit.'

The co-pilot moved over to the pilot's seat but found that the control column was inoperable. He went back to his seat.

'About this time I realised the blood I had been rubbing from my left eyelid and brow was not someone else's, but my own.'

McNatt jettisoned the bombs, pointed the PV-1 towards Kwajalein, and its longer runway, put Thomas Reed in the pilot's seat and instructed him on how to work the brakes. The co-pilot subsequently made a full flaps landing while Reed worked the brakes, the PV-1 rolling down the runway and eventually coming to a stop. It was then that he admitted to the crew that he had just made his first landing in a Ventura.

Alderson was operated on, had a lung removed and was evacuated to the US. Colgrove was treated in an adjoining room and returned to the unit a few days later, while McNatt was treated for shock and had several metal fragments removed from beneath his left eyebrow.

Back on Tarawa, VB-142 staged a major attack on the Japanese-held island of Nauru. In the largest strike ever conducted by a Navy PV-1 unit, Lt Cdr Clayton Miller scrambled all 15 Venturas and hit the island before dawn, causing major damage to the airfield and installations without losing an aircraft.

JALUIT

On 17 May 1944, Lt W E Scarborough of VB-144 led a three-aeroplane raid on Jaluit Atoll. The purpose of this mission was to strafe anti-aircraft positions and to search for any activity at the seaplane base, which US intelligence thought might be used to stage attacks against Allied forces. The Venturas flew over the atoll in line-abreast formation at tree-top height, passing over anti-aircraft positions as they went. Enemy gunners opened up with both light and medium flak. Lt Scarborough recalls:

'I decided to make another pass to try to get a better look, and directed the other aeroplanes to continue their search while I circled the island. I climbed higher to get a better view, and to be able to dive at a sufficient angle so as to bring the nose guns to bear on the enemy flak positions.'

Scarborough's gunners also directed their fire on any targets of opportunity that they could find as the pilot aimed for the atoll with the engines opened to full throttle and the PV-1 approaching a speed of 250 knots (287mph or 463 km/h) indicated.

'As we crossed the beach line, I saw the enemy gun emplacement ahead and opened fire with the bow guns. During the brief seconds of our approach, I was aware of my guns hitting all around the enemy position, and was very much aware of a lot of tracer coming our way! After passing the enemy position I stayed low and headed out into the lagoon, intending to head on after the other aeroplanes and continue the mission.'

Scarborough did not get the chance as his Aeroplane Captain pointed to the port engine, which was on fire. The pilot informed the crew to standby for ditching as the PV-1 headed over the atoll and out towards a lifeguard destroyer lying ten miles (16 km) offshore. When Scarborough throttled back on the port engine the fire went out, and an inspection showed no other damage, so he headed for Kwajalein, where after landing safely, the port engine stopped on the runway. The groundcrew found that a single 13 mm projectile had missed the propeller and hit a lower front cylinder. It penetrated the cylinder, wrecking the piston, then exited and hit the exhaust and intake manifolds.

Raids against by-passed islands by VB-144 continued throughout May and June 1944. Sometimes, flying bombing missions at tree-top height was detrimental to a Ventura crew's health. For example, on 9 June

PV-1 *"I'LL GET BY"* was based at Tinian in 1945, and may have belonged to VPB-133, as the unit adorned all of its aircraft with the titles of hit songs from the period. The identity of the individual in the photograph remains unknown (*via Author*)

Lt J O Brady's PV-1 had one of its engines knocked out and a crewmember wounded when it was hit by bomb fragments dropped from its own ordnance during an attack on Jaluit. Eight days later Lt D M McAusland found out about the accuracy of Jaluit's gunners when his PV-1 took three 20 mm hits. He was wounded, the hydraulic system shot out, the port rudder cable severed, the port engine damaged and the instruments put out of action. However, McAusland managed to make a wheels-up landing at Kwajalein.

The invasion of the Mariana Islands (Operation *Forager*) began on 14 June 1944. The Marianas consist of 15 islands that stretch 425 miles across the Pacific. The four largest, Saipan, Tinian, Rota and Guam, were the primary targets of the invasion. With Saipan taken, USAAF flying B-29 Superfortresses would have a base close enough to bomb the Japanese mainland. Opposing the invasion force were 32,000 Japanese defenders and, for the first time, American forces would also confront Japanese civilians. Before Saipan was declared secured on 9 July, there would be 16,500 American casualties, including 3400 killed.

During July VB-144 transferred to Roi-Namur, where it worked with Marine Air Group (MAG) 31 carrying out bombing and photographic reconnaissance missions. In September, the unit's tour of duty came to an end. Although VB-144 had been primarily used in the anti-submarine warfare role, its crews had also flown 339 bombing sorties that had seen them drop 395 tons of bombs on enemy-held territory, 20 ASW hunter-killer sorties, 42 special searches, eight reconnaissance flights and eight propaganda leaflet missions. Some months later, VPB-144 would return to the Pacific equipped with the PV-2 Harpoon.

Relieving the unit was VPB-133, commanded by Lt Cdr Ellyn L Christman. Nicknamed 'The Hit Paraders', its Venturas were adorned with artwork depicting hit songs of the period. Christman's PV-1 (BuNo 49599), nicknamed *Going My Way*, was adorned with a scantily clad woman sat on a fence rail, her thumb extended out towards the nose of the aeroplane. The unit had completed a previous tour in the Caribbean.

From October 1944 through to February 1945, VPB-144 conducted combat missions against Wake Island and Nauru (Caroline Islands), as well as daily reconnaissance flights to Kusaie (Marshall Islands).

Also arriving in-theatre at about the same time were the 'Devilfish P-Viators' of VB-150, which began operations from Tarawa on 10 July 1944. Flying aircraft adorned with an octopus, whose tentacles draped over the sides of the fuselage and whose head was formed by the top turret dome, VB-150 was the most easily recognisable Ventura unit to see action in the Pacific. After conducting a series of strikes against by-passed islands, it moved to Tinian's North Field on 28 August, where it flew reconnaissance flights to Woleai Island, ASW sweeps and bombing missions on Pagan Island until 5 March 1945.

TINIAN AND IWO JIMA

On 5 March 1945 VPB-133 transferred to Tinian and relieved VPB-150, the latter unit transferring six of its octopus-adorned aircraft to the newly arrived squadron. Commencing operations with FAW-1, VPB-133 flew daily 400-mile (643-km) searches that included frequent reconnaissance of Woleai, Puluwat and other islands in the Caroline group. On 23 March a

detachment of six aircraft from VPB-133 was sent to recently captured Iwo Jima to spearhead attacks on Japanese picket boats. These vessels were strung out from the Japanese mainland, and served as an early warning system for incoming B-29 raids.

Navy PB4Y-1 Liberator and PB4Y-2 Privateer units had been conducting attacks against the vessels, but the slow and unmanoeuvrable heavy patrol bombers were being mauled by the heavily armed boats. FAW-1 duly devised a plan where rocket-equipped PV-1s would team up with the PB4Ys to attack such vessels, Liberator or Privateer crews locating the picket boat and calling in Venturas to execute an attack.

In theory, and in practice, it was a sound plan, for the Venturas could fire their rockets from a safe distance, whereas the patrol bombers had to pass over the ships when strafing and bombing. The first successful attacks occurred on 14 March when Privateers from VPB-106 teamed up with two rocket-carrying PV-1s from VPB-151 to destroy two picket boats. One PB4Y-2 sustained serious damage to its control cables and a cannon shell seriously wounded two crew members.

Thirteen days later, a PB4Y-1 from VPB-102 joined three PV-1s of VPB-133 in attacking a picket boat operating between Honshu and the Bonin Islands. The ship was heavily armoured, with four turrets and numerous machine gun positions, and as the PV-1s came in to attack, it sent up a heavy screen of defensive fire. Pilot Lt(jg) Wilson and co-pilot Ens McCarthy were seriously wounded during their strafing pass, forcing enlisted crewman Henry M Saddler to take over the controls and successfully fly the PV-1 back to base.

On 3 April a patrolling PB4Y-2 of VPB-118 located targets 22 miles (35 km) from its position, and these turned out to be two picket boats spread 100 yards (91 m) apart. The pilot called in three PV-1s from VPB-133, which arrived an hour-and-a-half later. The Venturas attacked, firing 23 5-in rockets and strafed from 3500 ft (1066 m), and although the rockets missed, the ships took hits from the 0.50-cal nose guns. The Privateer followed the PV-1s 45 seconds later, and it too missed with its three bombs,

Octopus-adorned Ventura BuNo 34991 of VPB-133 was inherited from VB/VPB-150 (dubbed the 'Devilfish P-Viators') when the latter squadron departed Tinian in March 1945 (*via Daryl Hahn*)

VPB-151's PV-1 BuNo 49418 is seen conducting a sortie from Tinian. This aircraft was regularly flown by the unit's Crew Four (*via Daryl Hahn*)

although the gunners in the PB4Y-2 raked the bow and deckhouses of the vessels.

The picket boats responded to the attack by sending up accurate fire from 12.7 mm machine guns, the Privateer suffering 13 hits to the port wing and fuselage, which knocked out the number two engine and forced it to break off the engagement, although the PV-1s continued their strafing runs. However, they too failed to sink either ship, and all three Venturas were seriously damaged by flak before returning to Iwo Jima.

GOING TO JAPAN

In May 1945 'The Hit Paraders' added searches of the Japanese mainland to their operations. On the 14th, Lt Amos Wooten sortied at dawn with his crew in *Sentimental Lady* from Iwo Jima on a single-aeroplane reconnaissance flight to Japan. Allen E Honeycutt, an enlisted member of the crew, recalls the mission:

'We hit the coast just north of Shingu and found what appeared to be a small river, so we followed it inland. Suddenly, we came out into a large inlet or bay, which had 12 to 15 picket boats and island freighters anchored within it. Lt Wooten exclaimed, "We've caught them by surprise", so we made several runs, strafing and firing our rockets, which sunk at least three ships.

'The only way out of this bay was over some hills and then through a small cut towards the ocean, or by returning the way we had come. We elected to go through the cut since we were flying so low, and we banked and headed through the gap. As I looked out the side of my turret, I could see the anti-aircraft guns firing at us, but I had been instructed to hold my fire in case we encountered Japanese fighters. All of a sudden the aeroplane vibrated, and a huge hole appeared in the port wing just beyond the engine. Luckily, although the hit was in a gas tank, we did not catch fire, but we knew we would not have enough fuel to return to Iwo. Lt Wooten gave us the choice of returning to the coast of Japan and bailing out, or heading out to sea and taking our chances ditching. We chose the latter.

'"Mayday-Mayday-Dumbo" we called. First we contacted a Dumbo sub, and he gave us the location of Dumbo destroyer USS *Cummings*. Now we started getting rid of all the extra weight we could. I went into the nose section and stripped the "fifties", handing what ammo was left up to Lt Doster (James A Doster). Reiss (Elmore A Reiss, ARM2/c, nicknamed "PeeWee") dismantled the unnecessary radio equipment, Barrie Richardson (ARM2c, nicknamed "BD") removed the ammo and guns from the top turret and Laurion (Gilbert A Laurion, AMM2/c, nicknamed "Gil") did the same with his 0.30-cals in the tail section.

'Not knowing how long we would be adrift, I tied up the legs of my flightsuit and started to put the necessities down my pants legs. I remembered the Very pistol, and 10 or 12 flare cartridges, several cans of "C" rations and a large knife. Then I strapped on my 0.38 pistol and all the ammo that I could find.

'We all settled back to see how far we could get away from Japan. Eventually, we heard the pilot call, "Dumbo this is Peter Victor One. We have a visual on you. Take your ditching stations, here we go."

'It seemed to take hours to descend down to the water, but then we hit the sea. Crash! Like a rock skipping across a still pond, we were airborne again. The lower part of the aeroplane tore off, and Laurion, thinking we were down, jumped out. Up we went again, only to hit the sea for a second second time nose first. Richardson and I were braced against the door leading to the radio area, and when we hit we both shot through the door, flat on our backs, into the radio section.

'I remember saying, "Get the hell off me!" Then giving him a push; the momentum pushed him up and almost through the astro hatch. Now the aeroplane was knee deep in water. Wooten, Doster and Reiss all evacuated out the front, and Laurion was 50 to 100 yards behind the aeroplane swimming like hell to catch up. As I reached the astro hatch someone yelled, "Get a life raft". I jettisoned the door, reached over with my left hand and threw the six-man raft out some five to seven feet from the PV-1 with one hand – later, when I tried to pick one up, it was all I could do to lift it with both hands, yet I had thrown this one with just one hand!

'I then jumped in the water and started to swim away from the aeroplane. I was, and still am, a good swimmer, but for some reason the harder I swam I kept going down. Then I realised that I had all the extra weight in my pants legs, and had not inflated my Mae West.

'We immediately inflated the raft, and Wooten, Doster, Richardson and myself climbed on. To the rear, we could see Laurion move towards us. In front, Reiss, who could not swim a stroke, had put his Mae West on too tight, and when he inflated it, his face was pushed forward into the water. He would stroke, pull his head up, gasp for breath, and stroke again. All this time we were yelling, "Swim 'Pee Wee', swim!" He finally made it to the raft, as did Laurion.

'The destroyer *Cummings* arrived. From the starboard bow to amidships sailors threw big balls of rope at us. Several fell across the raft, which we grabbed, causing the raft to come alongside the destroyer, then over the side came the Jacobs ladder for us to climb aboard. As we started up the ladder, Lt Doster was in front of me, and he kicked me in the nose – I was the only casualty from this whole affair with a bloody nose.

'I guess the biggest disappointment for us was that we had been told that we would be given survivors' leave, which meant we could return to the States for several weeks. When a ship sinks, the crew is given this leave. What a rude awakening when we arrived back at Iwo – two days off, then back to flying.'

On 18 May Lt Walter M Genuit and his crew flew a search and strike mission to the coast of Japan near Shione Misaki Peninsula, on Kyushu, a distance of 620 nautical miles. Flying inland in the face of accurate enemy anti-aircraft fire, which damaged the aeroplane, Genuit hit radar stations, docks at Kushimete and an 80-ft trawler.

Conducting searches along the Japanese coast proved to be a deadly undertaking, as VPB-133 discovered on 27 May when it lost three aircraft. The first to go down was Lt Paul Schenk and his crew, who were also heading for Shione Misaki. Just hours later Lt(jg) Phillips reported that he had lost an engine while patrolling along the Japanese coast, and that he was returning home to Iwo Jima. His last voice contact with base was made when the PV-1 was still 300 miles (482 km) from Iwo. The third crew, led by Lt Cdr Coley, was luckier. Having had their PV-1 damaged whilst attacking a picket boat, they ditched about 300 miles from Iwo Jima and were rescued by the submarine USS *Tigrone* (SS-419).

Tragedy again struck 'The Hit Paraders' on 31 March. PV-1 BuNo 49599, flown by Lt Cdr Christman, took off from Iwo Jima on a routine search mission, and approximately three-and-a-half hours into the patrol, Christman spotted a picket boat. His co-pilot, Lt(jg) Perry A Litton, and radioman Ray Hurlbut (ACRM) recall what happened next:

'Our position was radioed to base and Lt Cdr Christman gave the order to prepare for attack. Zielanzy (Casey Zielanzy, AMM1c) manned the tail guns and Carroll (Bud Carroll, AOM1c) manned the turret. We attacked at a 30-degree angle, firing the wing-mounted rockets, and I saw two of the HVARs hit the boat. One hit the hull above the water line and the other appeared to penetrate the deck, although neither exploded.

'A second run was made in a futile attempt to damage the vessel with the depth charges. We had encountered enemy fire, and there were some holes visible in the fuselage and wings, but Lt Cdr Christman had no problem controlling the aircraft as we headed back to base.

'After landing, Lt Cdr Christman requested that the groundcrew rearm the aircraft with rockets and bombs, as well as refuelling it. He intended to return to the area and sink the picket boat, which he believed was damaged. The groundcrew chief advised him that we would not be allowed to fly without a structural check of the aeroplane due to it having been hit by enemy fire. Lt Cdr Christman felt that the damage was superficial, and he headed off towards the flight operations area saying "We flew the aeroplane in here, so we ought to be allowed back out for the kill".

'As Lt Cdr Christman and Lt(jg) Litton were leaving the operations tent, a P-51 Mustang that was in the process of landing ground-looped due to a heavy crosswind. The fighter crashed into a large cargo truck parked nearby, flipping it over and crushing Lt Cdr Christman, who had tripped over tie-down ropes while attempting to avoid the accident and fallen to the ground. Both VPB-133's CO and the P-51 pilot were killed.'

By early June, the detachment on Iwo Jima had returned to Tinian, where VPB-133 conducted occasional strikes against Puluwat, Woleai and the Lamotrek Islands.

HITTING BY-PASSED ISLANDS

VPB-151 began operations from Tarawa's Hawkins Field on 5 August 1944, before transferring to Tinian 24 days later. Prior to the transfer, the unit had conducted attacks on Narau and Jaluit. Once at its new base, VPB-151 sortied to Yap, Woleai, Rota and Pagan Islands. Attacking such by-passed islands was not always a 'milk run', and over the island of Woleai, the unit lost its only crew and aeroplane.

On 20 December 1944, two aeroplanes flown by Lts Sandy and Gardner had been sent to attack targets on Woleai, some 450 miles (724 km) south of Guam. Upon reaching the island, Lt Sandy attacked first, dropping a 500-lb (227-kg) bomb on a runway. The PV-1 was opposed by some light flak, but the aeroplane was not hit. Elmer Olsen, an enlisted member of Gardner's crew, recounts their run:

'We made a dive-bomb run on two small islands and got caught in a cross-fire, but the aeroplane wasn't hit. When we gained some altitude, we searched the sky for Sandy's aeroplane but could not find it. Gardner dropped his right wing and we saw fire on the water, which was no doubt caused by the crash of Sandy's aeroplane. Before heading back to Tinian,

Gardner flew over the spot and photographs were taken.

'There was no way of doing anything for them. We had no radio contact with Sandy, and Gardner told us that Sandy would take his radio earphones off when going into combat and put his hard hat (helmet) on.'

Between January and February 1945, VPB-151 flew advance air screen for the Fifth Fleet during the invasion of Iwo Jima, as well as conducting raids on the Japanese mainland. Then, between 13 and 19 March, a detachment of six aircraft was sent to Iwo Jima to fly anti-shipping sorties against picket boats in advance of Task Force 58.

PV-2 Harpoons began arriving on Tinian on 31 May 1945, VPB-142 (led by Lt Cdr John H Guthrie) debuting the type in-theatre. The unit had begun receiving PV-2s in January, but after arriving in Hawaii, wing spar problems had restricted the Harpoons to short-range reconnaissance flights. And for the first three weeks at Tinian, VPB-142 flew only routine patrols in areas void of enemy activity. Yet such sorties were deemed necessary in order to spot Japanese attempts to stop the American advance.

Since November 1944, the Japanese had been using submarines equipped with Kaiten human torpedoes to attack American shipping in the Central Pacific. On 27 June 1945, a Harpoon flown by Lt(jg) R C Jones spotted the fully surfaced I-165 some 480 miles (772 km) east of Saipan. The submarine, carrying Kaiten midget submarines, was on its way to attack US shipping in the Mariana Islands, and following a depth charge attack, two Kaitens, oil and debris were observed on the surface. This timely interception ended I-165's mission.

The second Harpoon unit to arrive in the Central Pacific was VPB-153, under the command of Lt Cdr Elliot M West. The squadron had been designated as a special unit controlled by the Training Task Force, for it had been given the job of testing a radar-guided bomb known as the Pelican. This weapon was designed to be used against submarines, but its homing signal was lost beyond 800 yards (731 m). After several unsuccessful tests, the project was terminated.

The unit then began training as a regular PV-1 bomber unit, and in February 1945 it transitioned to the PV-2 Harpoon. Plagued by structural failures, VPB-153's detachment deployment to Midway in May saw the squadron's PV-2s grounded, and it was not until June that routine searches recommenced.

Woleai Island, in the western Caroline Islands, was one of those enemy strongholds in the Central Pacific that was by-passed during the drive towards Japan. It was the job of PV-1 units to keep harassing the Japanese forces on these islands and atolls, and such raids were often met with anti-aircraft fire. Indeed, on one such heckling attack (on 20 December 1944) against Japanese troops on this very island, VPB-151 suffered its sole combat loss (*via Daryl Hahn*)

VPB-151 PV-1 BuNo 48807 is prepared for the fitment of 500-lb general-purpose bombs, seen sitting in front of the Ventura on their individual trolleys. This photograph was taken on Tinian, in the Mariana Islands, in the spring of 1945 (*via Daryl Hahn*)

Later that month the unit was sent to Agana, on Guam, where it came under the control of FAW-18. Search patrols out to 500 miles (804 km) began, but little was seen by this late stage of the war.

Despite contacts being few and far between come mid-1945, the Japanese continued in their efforts to supply their garrisons on the Pacific islands, although continued coverage by US search aircraft such as the PV-1/2 made it almost suicidal to do so. Dick Kallage of VPB-153 recalls searching the Caroline Islands every third day in PV-2 BuNo 37103, which never let him down. In particular, he remembers a night mission to Japanese-held Necker Island:

'Word came down that the Japanese were refuelling from tankers off shore. Our aeroplane was ready and it had three 500-lb (227-kg) bombs aboard. We took off at about 2300 hrs for the 800-mile (1287-km) flight. We took a radar expert with us, and when we got to the designated spot he said when to drop the bombs. We heard three loud shots and the aeroplane jumped, so we knew we had hit something. We were never told to go back, so I guess that ended the refuelling operation.'

PV-2 'Black Z101' served with VPB-142 in the Central Pacific, this unit (led by Lt Cdr John H Guthrie) arriving at Tinian on 31 May 1945. Operating as part of FAW-18, VPB-142 made only a modest contribution to the war effort with the Harpoon due to problems with the aircraft's wing spars. Indeed, it was restricted to flying short-range patrols and reconnaissance missions in areas known to be free of the enemy (*NARA via VP Navy*)

SURVIVORS OF THE USS *INDIANAPOLIS*

In April 1944 VB-152 had joined VB-153 as a special squadron under the control of the Training Task Force, testing the radar-guided Pelican. When the programme was dropped, it began training as a regular PV-1 unit, and from April to August 1945, it was based at Peleliu Island, in the Palau group. From here VPB-152 conducted anti-shipping sweeps, weather flights and rescue missions.

On 2 August, Lt Gwinn was on a patrol testing long-range antennas over the Pacific. The PV-1 was about 350 miles (563 km) from base, and crewman Joseph Johnson was reeling in a long wire antenna through the gunner's hatch in the rear of the aircraft, when the pilot, who was looking over his shoulder, spotted something on the surface of the water. As he hurried back to the cockpit, gunner Herb Hickman asked him what the problem was. Gwinn shouted, 'Look down and you will see'.

The pilot had spotted an oil slick, and he thought that he was onto a damaged Japanese submarine. He brought the aeroplane down close to the surface and followed the slick for 15 miles, thinking he would surprise the vessel. What he found surprised him. The slick was from the cruiser USS *Indianapolis* (CA-35), which had been sunk by the I-58 after secretly delivering the first atomic bomb to Tinian.

Of the crew of 1200 aboard the heavy cruiser, some 400 had gone down with the ship, but many more died from shark attacks before they were rescued. The 316 that were saved had been in the water for four days when Lt Gwinn discovered them. The pilot radioed their position back to base, and then remained in the area for as long as his fuel supply allowed. After circling for over two hours, and throwing anything they could to help the sailors, the crew returned to base with only 30 minutes of fuel remaining. Meanwhile, rescue craft had arrived at the site and retrieved the survivors.

Lt(jg) W G Gwinn of VPB-152 stands in front of his PV-1 (BuNo 49538). He was flying this machine when he spotted the survivors of the torpedoed cruiser USS *Indianapolis* (CA-35) on 2 August 1945. The other crewmen on this memorable sortie were Lt Warren Colwell (co-pilot), AOM2T Herbert Hickmann (turret gunner), AMM1c(T) Joseph K Johnson (radar operator) and William Hartman (Chief Radioman) (*via NARA*)

PACIFIC ALLIES

Although the US Navy was the primary operator of the Ventura in the Pacific, several units from both the Royal Australian Air Force (RAAF) and the Royal New Zealand Air Force (RNZAF) also saw action against the Japanese.

The only Pacific-based RAAF unit to both receive Venturas and use them operationally was No 13 Sqn, which began replacing its Hudsons with both ex-US PV-1s and home-built Beauforts in Canberra in July 1943. During its Hudson days, the unit had lost 80 per cent of its aircraft and had 220 aircrew killed in just six weeks whilst stationed at Ambon, in the Celebes, from 7 December 1941 to 30 January 1942.

Following the delivery of three Venturas, No 13 Sqn began training under the command of Wg Cdr Peter Parker. Between July and December, it continued to work up with both the Beaufort and Ventura, although a directive was issued to the unit on 17 December confirming that its composition would be changed solely to the Ventura. Despite this official edict, a detachment of Beauforts remained at Coffs Harbour conducting convoy coverage and anti-submarine sweeps until March 1944.

Three months later No 13 Sqn moved to Cooktown, in Queensland, and then on 25 August it flew to Gove, in the Northern Territory. The unit flew its first Ventura mission against Japanese shipping, supply dumps and installations around Dobo, in the Aroe Islands, on 10 September – six aircraft attacked in two waves, with all bombs landing in the target area. Although opposed by flak, all aeroplanes returned to base. From then on No 13 Sqn conducted convoy patrols and periodic attacks against enemy installations in the eastern Celebes.

During one such mission on 15 January 1945, Ventura A59-70 (ex-BuNo 48901), with Flg Off A G Goudie at the controls, was struck by

Combat-weary Ventura II A59-64 of the RAAF's No 13 Sqn is seen at Morotai in mid-1945. Some 75 Venturas were obtained by the Australian government through lend-lease, and post-war, most of the surviving airframes were sold for scrap between 1946 and 1949. Two, however, lingered on until February 1953 (*via Bruce Robertson*)

A No 13 Sqn Ventura undergoes routine maintenance under camouflage cover at Gove Airstrip, in the Northern Territory, on 9 December 1944. The unit flew a significant number of bombing missions from this site between August 1944 and March 1945 (*Queensland Air Museum via VMAF*)

gunfire whilst attacking enemy shipping in Bima Harbour at low level. The bomber's starboard engine had to be shut down and its guns and ammunition jettisoned. Thanks to careful fuel management, the aircraft returned safely to Gove, some 420 nautical miles away. The navigator who guided the bomber back to base was E G Gough Whitlam, who later became Prime Minister of Australia.

No 13 Sqn conducted 27 anti-shipping strikes off Timor in February 1945, and during these missions a number of enemy barges, and 300-ton merchant vessels code-named *Sugar Dogs*, were damaged or sunk. After March, the unit's activities ceased, and it moved to Morotai in June. On 16 August No 13 Sqn transferred to Labuan, from where it conducted supply drops and the evacuation of Australian PoWs. In December, the unit sent its remaining aircraft to Australia, and disbanded at Labuan the following month. No 13 Sqn suffered no combat losses with the Ventura.

No 13 Sqn's A59-61 (ex-BuNo 34992) suffered a collapsed port landing gear at Labuan on 24 September 1945. The aircraft, which had been received by the unit on 24 July 1944, was soon repaired and 'converted' (all of its armament was stripped out) into a transport the following month. Flown back to Australia in December 1945, the Ventura was placed in storage in October 1946 and eventually scrapped (*Queensland Air Museum via VMAF*)

KIWI VENTURAS

RNZAF Venturas were obtained through the Lend Lease Agreement signed by the US and New Zealand governments on 3 September 1943. Its PV-1s were shipped to Kaneohe, in Hawaii, where they were assembled and then flown to New Zealand by ferry crews from No 40 Sqn.

As with the US Navy, RNZAF Ventura units in the South Pacific primarily flew ASW sweeps, convoy patrols and harassing raids against the Japanese on New Ireland, Bougainville and New Britain. Ventura units, in addition to all RNZAF squadrons in-theatre, served under the control of No 1 (Islands) Group, which was a subdivision of Commander Aircraft South Pacific (COMAIRSOPAC). This was comprised of the Thirteenth Army Air Force, US Navy units and the 1st Marine Air Wing. And until 1945, local US commanders exercised control of RNZAF units.

The first unit to operate the aircraft was No 1 Sqn, led by Wg Cdr H C Walker, which began operations from Henderson Field, on Guadalcanal, on 23 October 1943. Failing to find the enemy during numerous patrols, the squadron moved to Munda, New Georgia, in November. Here, No 1 Sqn's missions consisted of routine patrols and searches, as well as bombing and strafing missions against Bougainville. Typical bombing attacks consisted of six Venturas loaded with six 500-lb bombs. Bombing was done from a few hundred feet, and followed up by strafing attacks.

On 10 December 1943 six Venturas of No 1 Sqn attacked copra warehouses being used by the Japanese at Arigua Plantation, on the

Pilot and co-pilot are seen at the controls of a Ventura during the long ferry flight from Hawaii to New Zealand in 1944. RNZAF Venturas were assembled in Hawaii by the US Navy and then flown to New Zealand by ferry crews (*via RNZAF Museum*)

Venturas NZ4513 and NZ4503 of No 1 Sqn fly over New Zealand's North Island during a training flight from Whenuapai in the autumn of 1943. Within weeks of this photograph being taken, the unit had headed north to Guadalcanal (*via RNZAF Museum*)

Armourers from No 10 Servicing Unit manhandle a 500-lb bomb towards a Ventura named *PATUA TE RA* at Henderson Field, on Guadalcanal, in late October 1943. This aircraft was flown by Flt Lt Spicer of No 1 Sqn (*via RNZAF Museum*)

eastern coast of Bougainville. They approached their target at 2000 ft (609 m) and dived to 500 ft (152 m) before releasing their bombs. Most fell either directly on or near the warehouses. Twelve days later two sections of Venturas attacked separate targets on New Ireland. Four aircraft bombed and strafed a lighthouse and radar station at Cape St George, but little damage was done to the targets, and two of the aircraft were severely damaged by flak.

On the same day, another six Venturas attacked enemy barges and other craft unloading at Ambitle Island, off the east coast of New Ireland. Arriving over the target, the Venturas broke off into three sections of two aircraft. The first section spotted a barge between Ambitle and Feni Islands and attacked with depth charges and bombs. Meanwhile, the second section targeted two camouflaged barges off Feni Island and Ambitle, scoring near misses.

SEARCH AND RESCUE

During the siege of Rabaul by Allied air forces, No 1 Sqn spent its time locating downed aviators. On 24 December two Venturas flown by Flg Off R J Alford and Flt Lt D F Ayson located a downed flyer in St George's Channel. Immediately, three Zekes jumped the PV-1s, and Alford and his crew damaged two fighters before making their escape into a cloud. Six to nine Zekes then attacked Ayson's aircraft, and in the melee that followed, the Ventura was badly damaged and Flg Off S P Aldridge was wounded. However, the number of fighters dwindled through the accurate gunnery of Ayson and his crew, Flt Sgt G E Hannah being credited with downing two fighters and WO W N Williams claiming a third.

A section of No1 Sqn Venturas had also been sent to Green Island from Guadalcanal on 29 October 1943, although they did not commence operations until 21 November. Here, crews teamed up with Marine PBJ Mitchell bombers to mount night heckling missions over Rabaul in an

This panoramic view of No 10 Servicing Unit's maintenance area on Bougainville in 1944 reveals not only American aircraft but also American vehicles too. In the foreground is NZ4518 and, in the background, NZ4503. All four Venturas visible in this photograph hail from No 1 Sqn (*via RNZAF Museum*)

effort to keep the Japanese base from conducting any offensive activities. No 1 Sqn, working in conjunction with American PBJs, co-ordinated the missions, which usually consisted of a flight of six to eight Venturas led by a PBJ bombing from 9500 to 13,000 ft (2895 to 3962 m). Additionally, low-level attacks were flown against targets on New Ireland.

No 2 SQN

Led by Wg Cdr A B Greenaway, No 2 Sqn languished at Espiritu Santo from November 1943 through to February 1944, before getting orders to move up to Munda. The unit then flew anti-submarine sweeps to the west and north-west (ranging out to a distance of 350 miles (563 km)) until April – it shared this mission with PV-1-equipped VB-140.

Enemy submarines were still numerous in the vicinity, particularly in the northern sector of the search area, and during one such sweep on 20 February, Flg Off Scott found a surfaced submarine between Green Island and New Ireland. Attacking it with four depth charges, he failed to inflict any damage on the submarine so left the area.

Later that same day, Flg Off Shuttleworth attacked another submarine in the same area. Although his depth charges would not release on the first pass, his gunners raked the deck and conning tower as the Ventura came around for another attack. The submarine submerged as Shuttleworth dropped four depth charges just ahead of the swirl left on the surface of the water. No debris appeared, however.

On the last day of February, No 2 Sqn conducted special operations against Japanese shipping and radar installations on Bougainville. Two aircraft, flown by Flt Lts Oliver and

Two Venturas from No 2 Sqn patrol along the coast of Bougainville in February 1944. Leading the two-ship formation is NZ4511 (ex-BuNo 33431). The RNZAF took delivery of 116 PV-1s and 23 B-34 Venturas in 1943–44 (*via Bruce Robertson*)

Fountain, hit a radar station at Adler Bay, on the eastern coast of the Gazelle Peninsula. Both aeroplanes made three bombing and strafing runs through medium and light anti-aircraft fire, placing ten of the bombs dropped in the target area. The station was severely damaged as a result of this attack.

A typical medium-level attack conducted by No 2 Sqn during this period was made against a truck depot at Rabaul on 11 February, the attacking force consisting of eight RNZAF Venturas and seven Marine PBJ Mitchells. The American formation bombed first, followed by the New Zealanders, who dropped their bombs after receiving a signal from by the lead PBJ. Approximately 90 per cent of the 16 1000-lb (453-kg) bombs and 48 325-lb depth charges exploded in the target area, leaving it covered with dense black smoke.

No 2 Sqn's heaviest attack was against Monoitu, in south-west Bougainville, on 28 February. This raid came about when Australian Intelligence operatives discovered a large concentration of enemy transport, supplies and troops in the area. Eight aircraft, each carrying 4000 lbs of bombs, arrived over Monoitu and then made one dummy run to make sure that they were over the right area. The Venturas then swung back around and 16 1000-lb (453-kg) and 48 500-lb (227-kg) bombs were dropped. Only two bombs failed to hit the target.

No 2 Sqn focused once again on anti-submarine sweeps in March and April, and several enemy vessels were sighted and one was attacked. On 5 March, Flt Lt Hamilton depth-charged a surfaced submarine east of New Ireland, the stick of bombs straddling the vessel. As the aircraft circled, an oil slick 80 ft (24 m) in diameter appeared on the surface of the water, clearly revealing that the submarine had been damaged. Through April and into the first week of May, No 2 Sqn continued its ASW searches, combined with heckling raids on Bougainville and Buka. At the end of May 1944, No 9 Sqn relieved the unit in the front line.

Returning to the action from New Zealand in early January 1945, No 2 Sqn started its next tour of duty at Green Island (under the leadership of Wg Cdr W A Cameron) in early January 1945 with medium-level bombing attacks and night heckles against Rabaul. In the middle of the month an American PBJ unit departed the island, leaving No 2 Sqn as the sole bomber unit on the base.

During this period, all attacks were made at low level, the aircraft dropping bombs fitted with 24-hour delayed fuses. Additionally, some enterprising crews loaded other non-traditional ordnance aboard Venturas. RNZAF crews on night heckles borrowed an idea from the Americans when they dropped empty bottles, which made a noise like whistling bombs. During the unit's tour, it took part in 31 daylight raids and ten night heckles against Rabaul.

No 2 Sqn was transferred to Jacquinot Bay, on the southern coast of New Britain, in June 1945, and then spent its first three weeks flying practice bombing and familiarisation flights over the area, before starting combat operations on 14 July. Through to war's end, the unit carried out a series of medium-level bombing attacks mainly against targets on the Gazelle Peninsula, and on islands off the northern coast of Bougainville. After VJ Day No 2 Sqn flew security patrols over Rabaul and New Ireland, and dropped surrender pamphlets over Japanese positions.

No 3 SQN

After replacing its Hudsons with Venturas, No 3 Sqn returned for a second tour of duty in May 1944, led by Wg Cdr I G Morrison. For the next three months, the unit spent its time flying ASW sweeps and convoy patrols from Espiritu Santo and Guadalcanal, although it failed to make any contact with the enemy. In August No 3 Sqn arrived at Los Negros, where it replaced No 9 Sqn, conducting weather flights and the occasional bombing raid on New Ireland. However, in October, the unit moved to Emirau Island to relieve VB-148.

Smoke rises from numerous explosions as Venturas from No 3 Sqn bomb Rabaul in May 1945. Operating in conjunction with Marine PBJ Mitchell units, RNZAF PV-1s 'kept the lid' on this by-passed Japanese fortress through to VJ Day (*via RNZAF Museum*)

By the end of the following month No 3 Sqn had become responsible for daily patrols to the north of Emirau, its crews seeking out possible Japanese shipping on the supply route from Truk to New Britain and New Ireland. Three aircraft took off each morning and covered an arc from the north-west to the north-east out to a distance of 300 miles (482 km) from their base. However, no enemy contacts were made.

No 3 Sqn arrived on Guadalcanal for its third tour in February 1945, and carried out ASW sweeps and yet more convoy patrols. The unit moved to Green Island in March, where it relieved No 2 Sqn. In April its Venturas were fitted with a bombsight suitable for medium-level bombing, and its crews began leading missions. Thereafter, it was no longer necessary for RNZAF formations to be led to a target by a Marine PBJ.

On 8 April, six RNZAF Venturas of No 3 Sqn led a bombing mission for the first time when they attacked Vunakanau, on the Gazelle Peninsula. Wg Cdr Morrison led the formation and Flt Lt Kidson was his bomb-aimer. The target area was thoroughly saturated, and all aircraft returned safely to base. In June, No 3 Sqn moved to Jacquinot Bay, although operations from this new base were at first restricted by a lack of bombs! The unit remained at Jacquinot Bay until 28 June, when it returned to New Zealand, having completed its tour. During No 3 Sqn's three weeks at the latter base, its flying had consisted chiefly of photographic sorties over the Bismarcks.

Nine Venturas of No 3 Sqn head for Rabaul in an impressive formation in May 1945. By this stage of the war the Japanese posed no aerial threat in the South Pacific, hence this 'peacetime' formation for the benefit of the camera (*via RNZAF Museum*)

Nos 4, 8 AND 9 SQNS

No 4 Sqn spent nearly four years (1940–44) at Nausori, in Fiji, conducting ASW sweeps and escorting ships. By late 1943, the danger posed by enemy submarines in the Fiji area had been eliminated, and the unit spent most of the next year function-

ing as an operational training

squadron. In September 1943, No 4 Sqn had discarded its Hudsons and re-equipped with Venturas, which were flown up from New Zealand.

The days of flying monotonous patrols from Fiji ended when the unit moved to Emirau in two echelons on 17 and 23 November 1944. During its three months here, No 4 Sqn dropped a total of 351 tons of bombs on huts, buildings, bridges, roads and anti-aircraft positions on New Ireland.

No 8 Sqn was formed in October 1944, and it commenced uneventful anti-submarine patrols from Fiji the following month. Based on Guadalcanal in January–February 1945, No 8 Sqn duly flew reconnaissance flights from Emirau until it disbanded in March 1945.

No 9 Sqn, commanded by Wg Cdr A C Allen, left New Zealand for Espiritu Santo in February 1944, and took over the duties of anti-submarine and escort patrols from No 2 Sqn when the latter unit moved up to Munda. In May, the squadron transferred to Piva, on Bougainville, and began bombing and strafing nearby targets of opportunity on the Gazelle Peninsula and Rabaul. No 9 Sqn was relieved in August and returned to New Zealand.

The unit commenced a second combat tour with the Ventura in January 1945, conducting operations from Fiji and Emirau before disbanding in June.

Personnel of No 4 Sqn pose with Ventura NZ4674 at Guadalcanal on 5 June 1945. By then, this unit was one of several RNZAF Ventura squadrons flying harassing missions against enemy bases on New Ireland and New Britain (*via RNZAF Museum*)

'Bombs away' as RNZAF Venturas strike Rabaul on 19 June 1945. On the receiving end were approximately 80,000 to 90,000 Japanese troops holed up on the island fortress (*via RNZAF Museum*)

US NAVY ATLANTIC SQUADRONS

The PV-1's superior speed and armament made it an obvious choice for protecting shipping lanes against German U-boats, which roamed the coasts surrounding North America at will following the US declaration of war in December 1941. By late 1942, American and Canadian air forces, equipped with such aircraft as the Hudson, Liberator and Catalina, were slowly in the process of eliminating this threat to merchant shipping. And in December of that year, PV-1 units of the US Navy commenced operations. In 1943–44, these squadrons would sink six U-boats in the Atlantic, Mediterranean and Caribbean.

To protect the Atlantic sea lanes, bases for PV-1 units were established at such locations as DeLand in Florida, Boca Chica at Key West, Floyd Bennett Field in New York, Beaufort Point in South Carolina, Quonset Point on Rhode Island and in Reykjavik, Iceland. In the Caribbean, bases were established at Guantanamo Bay in Cuba, San Juan, Puerto Rico, Brazil and Trinidad.

The Atlantic and Caribbean theatres were divided among six Fleet Air Wings, namely FAW-5, -9, -11, -12, -15 and -16. In all, 15 PV units were formed for Atlantic operations – VB/VPB-125, -126, -127, -128, -129, -130, -131, -132, -133, -134, -141, -143, -145, -147 and -149.

ATTACKS ON U-BOATS

The first Atlantic-based PV-1 unit to successfully attack a U-boat was VB-125. Originally formed as VP-82, and equipped with the Hudson, it had been sent to Quonset Point on 27 September 1942 to operate PV-3 Venturas (the Navy designation for the RAF's Ventura II) until PV-1s became available in December. Based at Argentina, in Newfoundland, and operating as part of FAW-12, the unit began ASW and convoy coverage.

On 27 April 1943 PV-1 125-B-6, piloted by Lt Thomas Kinaszczuk, attacked U-174, commanded by Oberleutnant Wolfgang Grandefeld, after it had been spotted on the surface off Cape Race, Newfoundland.

Ventura 125-B-6 of VB-125, flown by Lt Thomas Kinaszczuk, was used to sink U-174 on 27 April 1943. The early version of the PV-1 retained the bombardier's station in the nose. Visible are the two fixed 0.50-cal machine guns, which were supplemented in later models with a chin package of three more 'fifties' (*via NARA*)

Approaching the submarine, the bomber came under intense flak, which seriously damaged it, but Kinaszczuk successfully dropped depth charges and sank the U-boat.

The demise of U-174 was the highlight of VB-125's combat career. On 4 July 1943 it transferred to Boca Chica, then to San Julian, in Cuba, and finally Natal, in Brazil, where it remained until relieved by VPB-145 in March 1945.

VB-127, commanded by Lt Cdr William E Lentner Jr, began conducting ASW sweeps and convoy protection from Natal in May 1943 in conjunction with VB-129. For the next two months, the unit sent out two or three patrols a week without making contact with a single U-boat. On 21 June an eight-aeroplane detachment was sent to Fortaleza, again in Brazil, and it operated from here until the end of VB-127's tour.

The crew of 125-B-6 pose in front of their bomber, which has been decorated with the silhouette of a U-boat in white beneath the cockpit (this marking was identically positioned on the port side too). Lt(jg) Thomas Kinaszczuk (left) was the pilot on this historic mission. The window used for photographic reconnaissance is clearly visible on the underside of the aircraft (*via NARA*)

On 7 July Lt Cdr Lentner turned over command to Lt Cdr Richard L Friede, who remained in control until the end of the unit's tour. Routine patrols were interrupted on 30 July when Lt(jg) W C Young and crew sank U-591, commanded by Oberleutnant Raimer Ziesmer, off Recife, Brazil. The USS *Saucy* picked up 28 of U-591's 49-man crew.

Serving as part of FAW-16, VB-127 suffered from a lack of spare parts, and severe maintenance problems were noted. Indeed, these problems contributed to the death of a crew when, on 1 August 1943, Lt J R Marr lost power in the starboard engine of his PV-1 (BuNo 29920) and it crashed on take-off, killing five and injuring five others. On 6 September the VB-127 transferred to Port Lyautey, in Morocco, and commenced ASW sweeps with FAW-15. At the end of the month a detachment was sent to Agadir to conduct ASW sweeps around the Canary Islands.

Sitting on a snow-covered ramp at NAS Argentia, in Newfoundland, in December 1942 are five PV-1s of VB-125. These newly delivered aircraft are painted in Scheme II ASW camouflage, which was ideally suited to the arctic conditions of the North Atlantic. De-icing boots along the leading edges of the wings and tailplane were a necessity in this harsh climate (*via NARA*)

Conducting patrols near neutral Spanish territory could be dangerous, as two Ventura crews from VB-127 found out on 30 October 1943 when two Spanish CR.42 biplane fighters intercepted PV-1s flown by Lt A C Berg and Lt(jg) W C Young off the Canary Islands. During this brief encounter, in which gunfire was exchanged, the American gunners damaged one of the fighters, which had to make a forced landing.

German U-boats continually tried to break into the Mediterranean, but allied ASW tactics proved unbeatable. For example, on 24 February 1944, a VB-127 aircraft participated in the destruction of Oberleutnant Horst Geider's U-761 when Lt P L Holmes and an RAF No 202 Sqn Catalina attacked the vessel with depth charges. Damage to the submarine was so severe that it was later scuttled off Tangier, in Morocco.

DEADLY BATTLE

Before serving a tour in the Pacific, VB-128 had searched the Atlantic for U-boats. Commissioned on 15 February 1943, the unit had become the first Navy PV-1 squadron to fly the type operationally. Commanded by Lt Cdr Charles L Westhofen, VB-128 commenced operations from Floyd Bennett Field in May 1943.

Early on the morning of 7 August, an enemy submarine was spotted 300 miles (482 km) east of Norfolk, Virginia. Lt(jg) Frederick C Cross and his crew were alerted and took off in Ventura BuNo 29909 at 0430 hrs. U-566, commanded by Hans Hornkohl, was picked up by radar at a distance of 12 miles (19 km). Coming out of cloud, the PV-1 was quickly hit by flak, which knocked out an engine and mortally wounded Lt Cross.

Although wounded, the pilot pressed on with his attack and dropped his depth charges, which just missed the U-boat. Heavily damaged by flak, the PV-1 was forced to ditch, and although Lt Cross, co-pilot Lt(jg) Thomas J Aylward Jr and radioman James A Welch managed to get out before the aeroplane sank, the turret gunner went down with the bomber. Unfortunately, Lt Cross died of his wounds before a Navy PBM seaplane rescued the crew – he was posthumously awarded the Navy Cross.

Back at base, the unit's executive officer, Lt Joseph M George, heard about the ditching and headed out in his Ventura. Later, a radio report was received stating 'Approaching scene of action'. They were not seen again. It is very possible that the submarine also brought down this aircraft as well. The U-566 survived for another two months until the crew was forced to scuttle it on 24 October 1943 in the North Atlantic after it had been damaged by six depth charges from a British Wellington aircraft.

Four days after the attack on the U-566, VB-128 moved to Reykjavik and began working with RAF Coastal Command.

On 4 October 1943 Lt Cdr Westhofen picked up U-279 south-west of Iceland, but before he could attack, the submarine submerged. Westhofen decided to leave and come back later to see if the U-boat had surfaced. One hour later, the vessel was spotted on the surface once again, and the PV-1 went after it. Despite heavy anti-aircraft fire, Westhofen made a low-level attack and dropped three depth charges across the length of the hull. The submarine disappeared, being replaced by survivors in the water. The PV-1 pilot came back around and machine-gunned the survivors struggling in the water. En route back to base, he turned to his co-pilot, Lt(jg) John Luther, and explained that a quick death by gunfire would be better than a slow one freezing. None of the U-boat's 48-man crew were rescued from the freezing waters of the North Atlantic.

By December 1943 the U-boats had been driven out of range of the Iceland-based Venturas. That same month Lt Cdr Westhofen was transferred, and Lt Cdr Groome E Marcus became the new skipper. Within weeks the unit had moved to Puerto Rico.

During the flight to Central America, a VB-128 crew had the distinction of breaking a long distance record for flying on one engine. Lt Thomas Warnagaris was a third of the way into the trip when his Ventura lost an engine. He flew the remaining 650 miles (1045 km) to Ascension Island on one R2800, thus breaking the record for long distance flying in a PV-1 with a single engine.

For the next five months, VB-128 conducted ASW and convoy patrols from Puerto Rico without making contact with the enemy.

CARIBBEAN CRUISE

VB-130 was commissioned in March 1943 at DeLand under the command of Lt Cdr G G Price. On 7 June it arrived in Puerto Rico to fly ASW sweeps and convoy patrol, and two weeks later, orders were issued sending it to Trinidad's Edinburgh Field, in the British West Indies. VB-130 operated under the control of the USAAF's 25th Bombardment Group (BG), which assigned all daily missions. Consequently, there was little need for the squadron to take the initiative to plan operations.

The unit's relationship with the USAAF, and a nearby Navy seaplane squadron, was quite strained throughout VB-130's time in Trinidad, with personnel feeling that they were being treated as 'step children'. It came as a constant shock to squadron pilots to see how comfortably housed, transported and amused the seaplane pilots were, while they waded in mud, stood in line for 'chow', spent hours waiting for inadequate transportation, took turns at one head (toilet) per 24 men and had to drink their beer with the Army!

Maintenance problems also resulted in the unit having, on average, only 25 per cent of its aircraft available on any given day. Therefore, for the next three months, the squadron flew, on average, only two missions per day. VB-130 blamed the Hedron (US Navy Headquarters) Squadron, which maintained the aircraft, for they were poorly trained and poorly led. Some of the problems noted by VB-130 included oil put in the fuel tanks, coke bottles and tools left inside engine cowlings, improper engine run ups and a lack of spare parts. One PV-1 became the source of spare parts, and was named *Hangar Lily*. Yet despite these maintenance problems, the unit managed to achieve some impressive results.

On 6 August 1943, a VB-130 aircraft flown by Lt(jg) Theodore M Holmes sighted the German submarine U-615 south-east of Curacao, in the Caribbean Sea. He made several runs at it despite heavy anti-aircraft fire, and dropped a number of depth charges, which severely damaged the U-boat. Soon after Holmes's attack, a US Navy blimp, two Navy PBMs from VP-204 and -205 and a B-18 from the 10th BG arrived to finish the vessel off. The following day 43 survivors were picked up.

On 14 August 1943 VB-130 bade a happy farewell to Trinidad and moved to Recife, in Brazil, to

Framed by a sailor with a fire extinguisher watching three of his buddies arm a 250-lb general-purpose bomb, this Caribbean-based Ventura starts up its engines prior to launching on yet another routine patrol. By the time this photograph was taken in 1944, Navy PV-1 squadrons had been relegated to flying routine searches for enemy submarines that no longer patrolled the eastern seaboard of the Americas (*USN*)

serve with FAW-16. Two weeks later, it began operating from airfields at Fortaleza and Sao Luiz, covering convoys and and occasionally attacking enemy submarines, although none were sunk. In May 1944 VB-130 headed back to the US. Some 18 months later it was sent to the Pacific.

MEDITERRANEAN OPERATIONS

When German submarines attempted to sail through the Straits of Gibraltar and into the Mediterranean Sea, FAW-15 began moving long-range patrol aircraft into the area. To counter the U-boat threat, the allies adopted the 'Swamp' tactic – once a U-boat was identified, the area would be packed with surface vessels and aircraft in an attempt to force the submarine to the surface. VB-132 was one of the units selected to conduct operations from French Morocco.

Prior to deploying overseas, the squadron had lost two aircraft and crews in operational accidents while at Boca Chica. Between August and November 1943, a detachment had been established at San Julian, before the unit moved to Quonset Point for HVAR training. On 24 December 1943 it transferred to Port Lyautey, in French Morocco.

As with many PV units, operational accidents continued to plague VB-132. Lt Edward P Wood and his crew of five were killed when their aircraft (BuNo 34790) plunged into the water off Port Lyautey on 10 January. Then, on 1 July, Ens Louie H Hatchett and his crew of four were killed when PV-1 BuNo 34789 crashed 20 miles north-west

PV-1s undergo maintenance in the open air at their Caribbean base in 1944. The Ventura units in-theatre suffered from a poor reliability throughout the war (via NARA)

A PV-1 of VPB-127 gets a wash down at NAS Port Lyautey, in French Morocco, after a routine patrol in May 1945. Salt-spray caused continual corrosion problems, and diligent washing of airframes after every flight helped keep this at bay. This PV-1 is a late-build machine fitted with a 0.50-cal machine gun package which replaced the bombardier's station. The emblem located in the middle of the forward fuselage is the Lockheed company logo (via NARA)

The Free French Navy began receiving ex-US Navy PV-1s in November 1944, with 37 having been delivered by war's end. These were used primarily for ASW patrols in the Mediterranean. This Free French PV-1 of Flotille 6F, camouflaged in US Navy Scheme II, is being refuelled at Agadir, in French Morocco, in 1945. 6FE (Flottille d'Exploration) was established in September 1943 (via ARDHAN)

VB-132 132-B-1, nicknamed *Thumper*, is seen on patrol off the Florida Keys in 1943. Navy crews often had the option of retaining the Disney characters that had been applied to their aircraft on the Vega production line, or adorning the PV-1s with other artwork. In a lot of cases the *Donald Ducks* and *Mickey Mouses* were replaced by scantily clad women that reminded the sailors of home! (*via US Navy*)

U-604 comes under attack on 30 July 1943 by Lt Cdr Thomas D Davies of VB-129. Note the two unmanned anti-aircraft guns pointing skyward aft of the conning tower, these having been hastily abandoned as the U-boat begins to submerge. Four Mk 47 depth charges were dropped from the Ventura, which badly damaged the submarine, causing it to be scuttled on 11 August (*via NARA*)

of Port Lyautey. Finally, on 16 October, Lt(jg) Thomas J Galvin and his crew of four died when their Ventura crashed near Naples, in Italy.

While based in French Morocco, VB-132 had been responsible for training the personnel chosen to staff Free French Patrol Squadron 1 (VFP-1), which was to fly the Ventura. Eventually, in November 1944, following the handing over of all of VB-132's aircraft, equipment and supplies to VFP-1, the unit returned to the US, where it began transitioning onto the PB4Y-2. The squadron was decommissioned in May 1945.

U-BOATS ESCAPE

Whilst operating in the Atlantic and Caribbean, PV-1s carried out a number of attacks against enemy submarines without actually sinking them. One such unit to experience this disappointment was Lt Cdr William C Murphy's VB-133, which began its overseas duty at San Juan with FAW-11 on 19 July 1943.

Just five days after arriving in Puerto Rico, Lt R B Johnson flew out over the Atlantic to investigate a submarine sighting reported by a Pan American Airways aeroplane. The enemy vessel was located on the surface, but in the excitement, Johnson forgot to open the bomb-bay doors and he had to make a second pass! The submarine was submerging by the time the Ventura pilot finally dropped a string of six depth charges, which straddled the vessel. The unknown U-boat managed to escape, however.

A Ventura crew from VB-129 also conducted an unsuccessful attack on a U-boat on 30 July 1943. Lt Cdr Thomas D Davies sighted U-604, commanded by Kapitanleutnant Horst Holtring, fully surfaced north-east of Bahia, in Brazil. Spotting the PV-1, the submarine opened up with 20 mm cannon fire, but the Ventura's nose guns swept the decks as Davies dropped four Mk 47 depth charges. The submarine submerged at a 60-degree angle, with its screws out of the water, and although the U-boat managed to survive this attack, it had to be scuttled 12 days later.

On 7 February 1944 VB-129 transferred to Quonset Point for convoy coverage and ASW sweeps, and it remained here until sent to Brunswick, in Maine. It was eventually disbanded on 4 June 1945.

VB-133 made another unsuccessful attack on 8 November 1943, by which time the unit had transferred to Curacao. And unlike the 24 July incident, the U-boat fought back. Duke Dillon, a radar operator with VB-133, remembers the engagement with the submarine:

'The skipper, Lt Cdr Murphy, and my pilot got a call to report to San Juan for a special meeting. After take-off, I was in the nose of the aeroplane watching the radar. Soon after leaving Curacao I called, "Captain I am getting a strange sighting on the radar". He asked "Where?", and we then honed in on the signal. The next thing I knew he said, "Make sure the bomb release is armed". This was also in the nose of the aeroplane.

'Things happened so fast, I had no time to get out of the nose. The nose guns were blasting – we made a bomb run on the sub. The sub did not make a run for it. Instead, it opened up with its anti-aircraft guns. We were soon hit by flak, and the skipper called, "Get up here now. We have been hit". I squeezed through where the co-pilot sat to enter the cockpit.

'We were still flying, although there was a big hole in the wing and one of the engines was smoking. What should we do? It was decided I would pump oil from the auxiliary oil tank and keep the engine running as long as possible. As luck would have it, we made it back to Curacao.'

The majority of Ventura and Harpoon units serving in North and South America never encountered the enemy, and instead fought a war of boredom. They flew tedious patrols over an empty ocean, and fought a battle to keep their aircraft in the air due to a lack of spare parts and occasionally poor maintenance. Although there were no casualties caused by the enemy, many men died in operational accidents.

One of the units assigned to this campaign was VB-126, which had started life as VP-93 flying the PBY-5A and Hudson, before transitioning to the PV-1 on 1 March 1943. Between December 1942 and June 1943, the unit was stationed at Argentia, in Newfoundland. By June, German U-boats had moved out of range of PV-1 search sectors and, for the next 13 months, the squadron was divided up between Quonset Point and Cherry Point. From January to March 1945, VB-126 was deployed in Brazil and on Ascension Island, operating as part of FAW-16. On 27 June 1945 VPB-126 was decommissioned.

Another Atlantic-based squadron was VB-133, whose PV-1 BuNo 33381, flown by Cdr Ed Lea and co-pilot Ward Tifft, had the distinction of flying non-stop from San Juan, in Puerto Rico, to Norfolk, Virginia – a distance of 1750 miles (2815 km). The purpose of this flight was to determine if a PV-1 could fly from San Francisco to Oahu, in Hawaii, a distance of 2090 miles (3362 km). The flight showed that even with added fuel tanks, the aircraft could not make it to Hawaii unrefuelled, but this sortie did nevertheless surpass the PV-1's maximum rated range of 1660 miles (2671 km).

A PV-1 from VPB-125 takes off from NAS Natal, in Brazil, on 25 April 1945. Visible beneath the wings are four 5-in HVARs. In the background are US Navy PB4Y-1 Liberators, which by 1945 had also been relegated to flying mundane convoy patrols following the collapse of the U-boat threat (*via NARA*)

Lt Glenn A Ottsman glances over his shoulder at the camera whilst at the controls of a VPB-129 Ventura in 1945. Patrols often lasted six to eight hours, with crews rarely spotting anything other than whitecaps on the surface of the ocean by this late stage of the war (*Lt Glenn A Ottsman via Ray Snodgrass*)

After completing its tour on 16 April 1944, VB-133 headed back to the US, where it reformed for a tour of duty in the Central Pacific.

SUPPLEMENTARY NAVY OPERATIONS

The Ventura was a tricky aircraft to fly, and some crews referred to it as the 'Flying Coffin' because of the number of people that were killed in operational accidents involving the PV-1. One such unit to experience this was VB-134, which suffered a series of losses after completing its training at DeLand. The worst of these accidents occurred on the very day (5 July 1943) the unit began transferring to NAS Boca Chica, in Key West, when the PV-1 piloted by Richard R Barnes crashed on take-off, killing all nine crew members aboard the bomber.

Following the completion of advanced training, VB-134 moved to Cherry Point to relieve VB-126. It remained here conducting convoy patrols along the eastern seaboard until 21 November, when the unit transferred to Quonset Point to undertake rocket training. This lasted until 24 January 1944, and during this period (on 5 December 1943) another crew, and five personnel on the ground, were killed when Lt Walter Craiaia's PV-1 was caught by a gust of wind and crashed into a hanger.

By 8 February 1944 VB-134 was operating from Recife, in Brazil, conducting dawn-to-dusk convoy patrols between Rio de Janeiro and Trinidad. In April, detachments were sent to operate from the Brazilian towns of Maceio, Fortaliza and San Luiz. That same month the unit began training members of Brazilian Air Group One in PV-1 operations at Recife. VB-134's final loss occurred on 18 December 1944 when Lt(jg) Wolfe and his crew were killed in a crash caused by the failure of BuNo 34993's port engine on take-off. An investigation later revealed that several of the unit's aircraft were suffering from severe mechanical problems.

VB-141 carried out ASW sweeps and convoy patrols between August 1943 and July 1944 while stationed at Guantanamo Bay and San Juan. Detachments were also sent to British Guyana, Trinidad, Curacao and Panama. During this time the unit suffered two operational losses, which resulted in the deaths of 11 men. On 13 November 1943 Lt(jg) Leck M Evans and his crew of four (in BuNo 34828) failed to return from a patrol. The following month, on the 22nd, Lt(jg) William W Lomas and his crew of five were killed while taking off on a patrol in BuNo 34590.

By July 1944 VB-141 was based at Beaufort, in South Carolina, and this was where Lt Dean H Ringgenberg and two crew members were killed in a mid-air collision on 5 October 1944. In February 1945 the unit sent a detachment to Brunswick to cover the northern convoy lanes, despite U-boats having been eliminated from the North Atlantic. In April, VPB-141 began transitioning to the PV-2, and until its demobilisation in June 1945, the unit performed the Air-Sea Rescue role along the eastern seaboard.

VB-145 was another PV unit to be based in the Caribbean between September 1943 and February

Empty rocket rails protrude forward of the wing leading edges of this VPB-129 Ventura, as it flies along the eastern coast of the United States in 1944 (*Lt Glenn A Ottsman via Ray Snodgrass*)

1945. It operated from Natal and later Recife, with detachments based at Fernando de Noronha Island and in the Ascension Islands. The unit lost three men on 29 July 1943 when a PV-1 piloted by Lt(jg) Broady crashed on the runway at DeLand. The co-pilot was killed in the crash, and Lt Broady and a passenger later died from burns. By March 1945, VPB-145 was back in the US operating from Brunswick, having been relieved by VPB-126.

VB-147 began its operational career in February 1944 on the eastern seaboard, flying ASW sweeps from Elizabeth City, North Carolina. During its training phase, two men were killed in aircraft accidents. In May the unit transferred to Trinidad, with detachments operating from Surinam and San Juan. From December 1944 through to May 1945, VPB-147 flew from Curacao, PV-2s arriving in April to replace the unit's worn out PV-1s. In June the squadron returned to Quonset Point, before being demobilised in July.

An aerial view of the ramp at Coast Guard Station Elizabeth, in New Jersey, in 1945. Note the parked PV-1s and PBY Catalinas, these types forming the backbone of the US Navy's ASW patrol fleet for much of World War 2 (*Lt Glenn A Ottsman via Ray Snodgrass*)

CLOSING THOUGHTS

The Ventura was not liked by the RAF, being seen only as an interim aircraft until the Mitchell, Boston and Mosquito became available in sufficient numbers to replace it. Air Vice Marshal Basil Embry of the 2nd Tactical Air Force did not mince his words about the aircraft, stating, 'The Ventura is thoroughly bad, being slow, heavy, unmanoeuvrable and lacking in good defensive armament'. Most RAF crews agreed with him.

To the British, the Ventura did not come up to the same operational standards as the Mosquito or Boston. The aircraft was chosen to participate in some of the most daring missions of the war, and was subjected to inclement weather, intense flak and aggressive enemy fighters. The Mk I and II were not as well armed as the later model PV-1/GR V, and this was certainly a contributing factor in the heavy losses suffered by the RAF.

Conversely, many American crews (with the exception of VMF(N)-531) seemed to have enjoyed flying the PV-1, regarding it as a sturdy, well-armed aircraft. Indeed, they saw the Ventura as well suited to armed reconnaissance, harassing missions and ASW sweeps against the Japanese.

The Ventura was ideal for operations in the Pacific theatre, but it did not live up to the standards required over Europe. Tactically, the US Navy, RAAF and RNZAF used the Ventura for armed reconnaissance, staging missions consisting of one to six Venturas, while the RAF flew multiple aeroplane raids of 12 to 21 aircraft against heavily fortified targets.

The Brazilians received 14 PV-1s in March–April 1944, which were issued with serials 5034 to 5047. These aircraft equipped *1° Grupo de Bombardeio Médio* (1st Medium Bomber Group) and were based at Recife. In 1945 six PV-2 Harpoons (serial numbers 5048 to 5051) were also received, which became part of *2° Grupo de Bombardeio Médio* (2nd Medium Bomber Group). The Brazilians continued to use the Harpoons into the 1950s, with some eventually being modified to serve as transports (*via Rudnei D da Cunha*)

APPENDICES

VENTURA/HARPOON UNITS OF WORLD WAR 2

United States Navy

Unit	Aircraft	Service Dates	Operational Area
VP-82	PV-3	10/1942-3/1943	Newfoundland
VP-93	PV-3	11/1942-12/1942	Newfoundland
VB/VPB-125	PV-1	4/1943-end of war	Atlantic Coast/Caribbean
VB/VPB-126	PV-1	1/1943-end of war	Atlantic Coast/Caribbean
VB/VPB-127	PV-1	2/1943-end of war	Caribbean/Mediterranean
VB/VPB-128	PV-1	2/1943-end of war	Caribbean/United States/South Pacific
VB/VPB-129	PV-1	2/1943-end of war	Caribbean/Atlantic Coast
VB/VPB-130	PV-1	3/1943-end of war	Caribbean/Atlantic Coast
VB/VPB-131	PV-1	3/1943-8/1945	Caribbean/Aleutian Islands
VB/VPB-132	PV-1	3/1943-end of war	Caribbean/Mediterranean
VB/VPB-133	PV-1	3/1943-end of war	Caribbean/Central Pacific
VB/VPB-134	PV-1	4/1943-4/1945	United States
VB/VPB-135	PV-1	2/1943-10/1944	Aleutian Islands
	PV-2	5/1945-end of war	
VB/VPB-136	PV-1	3/1943-3/1945	Aleutian Islands
	PV-2	5/1945-end of war	
VB/VPB-137	PV-1	2/1943-6/1945	Central Pacific/South Pacific
VB/VPB-138	PV-1	3/1943-5/1944	South Pacific
VB/VPB-139	PV-1	4/1943-5/1944	Aleutian Islands
	PV-2	2/1945-end of war	
VB/VPB-140	PV-1	4/1943-4/1944	South Pacific
VB/VPB-141	PV-1	6/1943-4/1945	Caribbean/United States
	PV-2	4/1945-5/1945	
VB/VPB-142	PV-1	6/1943-1/1945	Central Pacific
	PV-2	1/1945-end of war	
VB/VPB-143	PV-1	6/1943-11/1944	Caribbean/United States
VB/VPB-144	PV-1	7/1943-9/1944	Central Pacific
	PV-2	11/1944-end of war	
VB/VPB-145	PV-1	6/1943-6/1945	Caribbean/United States
VB/VPB-146	PV-1	7/1943-2/1945	South Pacific
	PV-2	5/1945-end of war	United States
VB/VPB-147	PV-1	8/1943-7/1945	United States/Caribbean
VB/VPB-148	PV-1	8/1943-10/1944	South Pacific
	PV-2	5/1945-end of war	Hawaii
VB/VPB-149	PV-1	9/1943-end of war	United States/South Pacific
VB/VPB-150	PV-1	9/1943-3/1945	Central Pacific
	PV-2	5/1945-7/1945	United States

VB/VPB-151	PV-1	1/1944-6/1945	Central Pacific
VB/VPB-152	PV-1	4/1944-end of war	Central Pacific
VB/VPB-153	PV-1	4/1944-1/1945	Central Pacific
	PV-2	2/1945-end of war	
VB/VPB-200	PV-1	4/1944-end of war	Hawaii
	PV-2	1/1945-end of war	
VD-2	PV-1	1943-end of war	United States

UNITED STATES MARINE CORPS

Unit	Aircraft	Service Dates	Operational Area
VMF(N)-531	PV-1	4/1943-5/1944	South Pacific

ROYAL AIR FORCE

Unit	Aircraft	Service Dates	Operational Area
No 13 Sqn	GR I/GR V	10/1943-12/1943	Britain
No 21 Sqn	Mk I/II	5/1942-9/1943	Britain
No 299 Sqn	Mk I/II	11/1943-1/1944	Britain
No 500 Sqn	GR V	12/1943-7/1944	Mediterranean
No 519 Sqn	GR I/GR V	9/1943-10/1944	Britain
No 521 Sqn	GR I/GR V	10/1943-12/1944	Britain
No 624 Sqn	Mk II	9/1943-10/1943	Britain

ROYAL AUSTRALIAN AIR FORCE

Unit	Aircraft	Service Dates	Operational Area
No 13 Sqn	Mk II/PV-1	6/1943-end of war	Australia/South Pacific
No 459 Sqn	GR V	12/1943-7/1944	Mediterranean
No 464 Sqn	Mk I/II	8/1942-8/1943	Britain

ROYAL CANADIAN AIR FORCE

Unit	Aircraft	Service Dates	Operational Area
No 8 Sqn	GR V	5/1943-5/1945	British Columbia
No 113 Sqn	GR V	4/1943-8/1944	Nova Scotia
No 115 Sqn	GR V	8/1943-8/1944	British Columbia
No 145 Sqn	GR V	5/1943-6/1945	Nova Scotia
No 149 Sqn	GR V	7/1943-3/1945	British Columbia
No 122 Composite Squadron	GR V	1943-end of war	British Columbia
No 34 Operational Training Unit	Mk I/II/GR V	6/1942-end of war	British Columbia
No 1 Central Flying School	Mk I/II	1943-end of war	Ontario

ROYAL NEW ZEALAND AIR FORCE

Unit	Aircraft	Service Dates	Operational Area
No 1 Sqn	PV-1	8/1943-5/1945	South Pacific
No 2 Sqn	PV-1	8/1943-end of war	South Pacific
No 3 Sqn	RB-34/PV-1	6/1943-6/1945	South Pacific
No 4 Sqn	PV-1	9/1943-end of war	South Pacific
No 8 Sqn	PV-1	9/1943-3/1945	South Pacific
No 9 Sqn	RB-34/PV-1	10/1943-5/1945	South Pacific
No 487 Sqn	Mk I/II	9/1942-8/1943	Britain

SOUTH AFRICAN AIR FORCE

Unit	Aircraft	Service Dates	Operational Area
No 17 Sqn	Mk I/II/GR V	6/1943-1945	Mediterranean
No 22 Sqn	Mk I/II/GR V	8/1942-end of war	South Africa/Mediterranean
No 25 Sqn	Mk I/II/GR V	9/1942-11/1944	South Africa/Mediterranean
No 27 Sqn	Mk I/II/GR V	8/1942-11/1944	South Africa/Mediterranean

FRENCH NAVAL AVIATION

Unit	Aircraft	Service Dates	Operational Area
Flotille 6FE	PV-1	11/1944-end of war	Mediterranean

BRAZILIAN AIR FORCE

Unit	Aircraft	Service Dates	Operational Area
1st Medium Bomber Group	PV-1	3/1944-end of war	Brazil
	PV-2	1945	

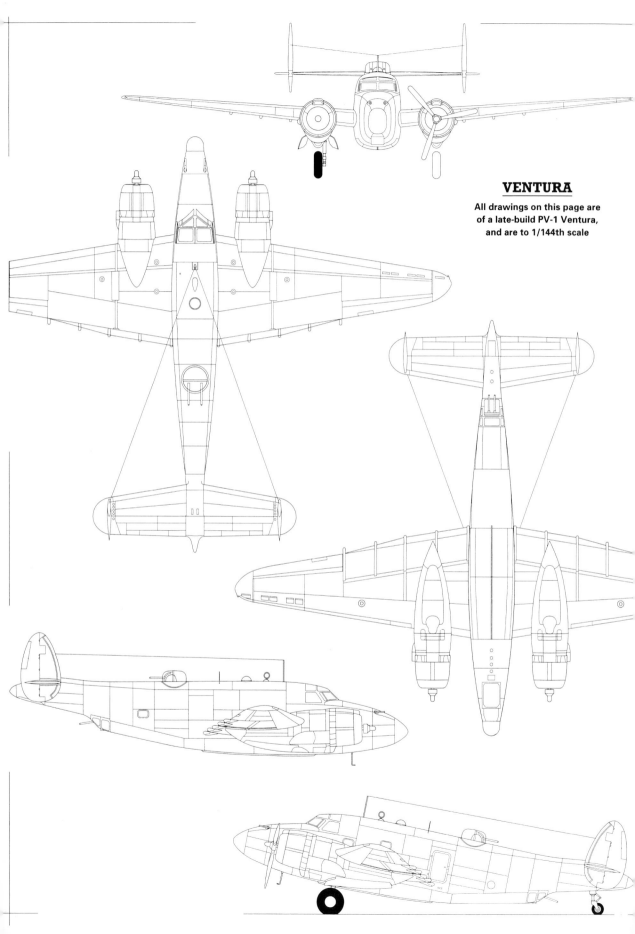

VENTURA

All drawings on this page are
of a late-build PV-1 Ventura,
and are to 1/144th scale

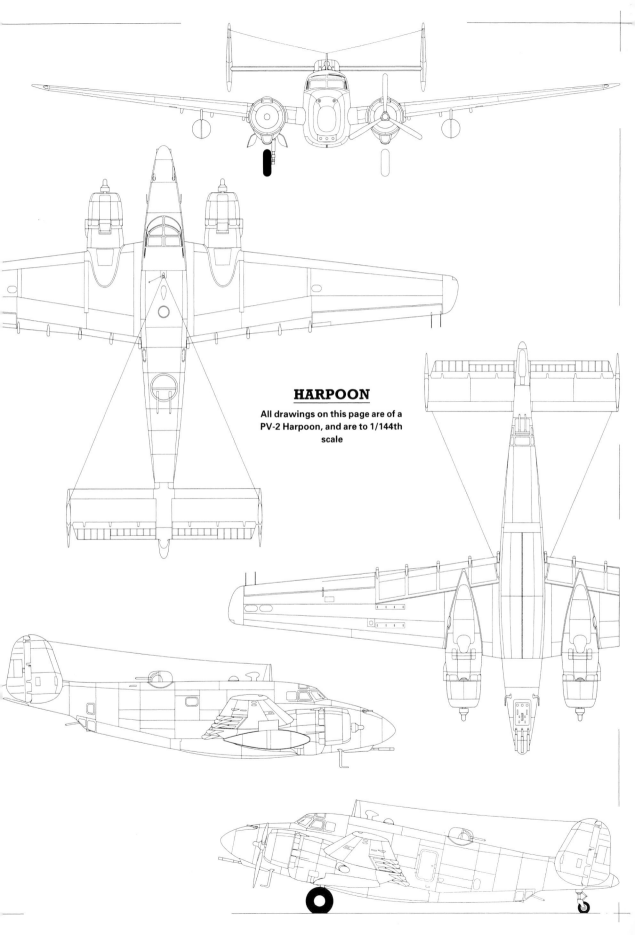

HARPOON

All drawings on this page are of a
PV-2 Harpoon, and are to 1/144th
scale

COLOUR PLATES

1

B-34/Ventura IIA AJ288, California, late 1941
Sporting sand and spinach camouflage and light grey undersurfaces, this B-34 was retained by the USAAC. Powered by two 2000 hp Pratt & Whitney R-2800-31 engines, the British-ordered Ventura IIAs featured the American designation B-34. The Mk IIA differed from the Mk I in respect to its armament, which was American instead of British. The most noticeable difference was the replacement of the bomber's 0.303-in machine-gun-equipped Boulton-Paul turret with a Martin upper turret boasting twin 0.50-cal machine guns. In addition, two flexible 0.50-cal guns replaced the 0.303-in weapons in the nose. Great Britain ordered 487 Ventura IIs but only 196 actually reached the RAF. After Pearl Harbor, the USAAF diverted 264 aircraft for its own use, retaining the RAF serials AJ235 through to AJ442. This aircraft features the RAF serial number AJ288 forward of the tail unit. In 1942 the RCAF received 45 B-34s for use with No 34 Operational Training Unit and No 1 Central Flying School. In May 1943, the RAAF was issued with 20 B-34s, and the following month the RNZAF took charge of 19 such aircraft.

2

Ventura I (prototype) AE658, Lockheed Vega plant, Burbank, 31 July 1941
British procurement of the Ventura began with the Mk I in September 1941. Sporting the American equivalents of dark earth and dark green camouflage, with light grey undersurfaces, the prototype flew for the first time on 31 July 1941. Although initially unarmed during its numerous test flights, the bomber was eventually fitted with eight machine guns. It was powered by two 1850 hp Pratt & Whitney S1A4-G Double Wasp engines, and could carry 2500 lbs of bombs in an internal bomb-bay. During test flights, the aircraft was not fitted with machine guns. The prototype was issued to the RCAF, and it served with No 34 OTU at Pennfield Ridge, New Brunswick, into 1943.

3

RB-34 NZ4600 (ex-RAF FD665) of No 3 Sqn, Fiji, July–October 1943
This Ventura was amongst the first 19 delivered to the RNZAF on 6 June 1943 in standard USAAF olive drab and light grey camouflage. However, the aircraft arrived in such a dilapidated condition that they were cannibalised to make just six airworthy. The RNZAF resprayed them with ocean blue upper and sky grey undersurfaces. The half-dozen RB-34s were initially assigned to No 3 Sqn, but were pulled from service in October 1943 when PV-1 Venturas began arriving. New Zealand-based Venturas had the titling *COASTAL PATROL* painted in white above the fuselage entry door. This particular machine has been restored, and is presently on

display at the Museum of Transport and Technology in Auckland, New Zealand.

4

PV-3 'Black B-11' (BuNo unknown) of VP-82, Argentia, Newfoundland, October 1942
In September 1942 the US Navy requisitioned 27 Ventura IIs from the British (serial numbers AJ511 to AJ537) and designated them PV-3, with Bureau of Aeronautics numbers 33925 to 33951. The aircraft retained British equipment and lacked a dorsal turret. VP-82 was the first squadron to receive PV-3s at Quonset Point, Rhode Island, in October 1942. This aircraft is painted in light grey anti-submarine camouflage, and features the national insignia used between May 1942 and June 1943. VP-82 carried out ASW and convoy patrols from both Argentia and Quonset Point, and in December 1942 exchanged its PV-3s for PV-1s. Many of the older Venturas were in turn sent to Operational Training Unit 2 (VB-2 or OTU-2). In April 1943 VP-82 was redesignated VB-125.

5

PV-1 'Black 125-B-6' (BuNo unknown) flown by Lt Thomas Kinaszczuk, VB-125, Argentia, Newfoundland, 27 April 1943
This early model PV-1 attacked the surfaced U-174 off Cape Race on 27 April 1943, and during the ensuing engagement the U-boat's 20 mm anti-aircraft guns heavily damaged it. The submarine was sunk, however, taking with it its captain, Oberleutnant Wolfgang Grandefeld, and his entire crew. Lt Kinaszczuk was awarded the Navy Cross for his exploits. Navy Ventura squadrons employed varying identification numbers on their aircraft which corresponded to the last two or three digits of the type's BuNo, or the squadron number followed by individual flight numbers assigned within the unit. The in-squadron number of this aircraft was B-11. Early-build PV-1s had two-tone camouflage consisting of blue-grey upper and light grey undersurfaces. The PV-1 was essentially the Navy version of the B-34/Ventura Mk II, with a few extra modifications. To improve patrol range, the fuel capacity was increased from the B-34's 1345 gallons to 1607 gallons, with this extra fuel being housed in two additional fuel tanks located in the aft bomb-bay. Two 155-gallon drop tanks were also installed under the wings. Finally, the PV-1 boasted Navy-specified electronic equipment, including the ASD-1 search radar.

6

PV-1 'Black X5' (BuNo unknown) flown by Lt(jg) L W Fischer, VB-135, Attu, Alaska, June 1943
VB-135 became the first Ventura squadron to operate in the Pacific when it arrived in Alaska in April 1943. Lt Fischer regularly flew this aircraft in 1943, and prior to returning to Attu in it from Adak

following a spell in maintenance, he purchased 20 cases of beer for the squadron and loaded them into the PV-1's bomb-bay. Inclement weather on the return flight forced him to land at Amchitka, where a routine hydraulic check was conducted by the headquarters squadron. The bomb-bay doors were opened and out dropped ten cases of the beer! PV-1 'X5' has the early-build eight-window bombardier's station, and displays a red nose cone containing the ASD-1 radar. This machine may have also served with VB-136 in 1943.

7
PV-1 'White/Black 13' (BuNo unknown) of VB-140, Solomon Islands, October 1943
In October 1943 VB-140 joined sister-squadron VB-138 in the Solomon Islands, and proceeded to conduct ASW sweeps and harassing missions against Japanese installations. Early PV-1s retained the bombardier's station in the nose until it was deleted in favour of a chin package housing three 0.50-cal machine guns. This aircraft features the national insignia on both the front and rear fuselage. Later PV-1s only had the rear fuselage marking.

8
PV-1 'Black 25' (BuNo unknown) of FAW-4, Attu, Alaska, June 1944
This Ventura has the distinctive FAW-4 'Empire Express' insignia and six mission markings on its fin. The FAW-4 insignia appeared on a handful of VB-135 PV-1s. This machine also has an 18-in loop antenna installed beneath the nose in an effort to reduce precipitation static.

9
PV-1 'Black 83' of VB-127 (BuNo unknown), Port Lyautey, French Morocco, February 1944
A small number of Navy Ventura units operated from Port Lyautey and Agadir, in French Morocco, conducting convoy patrols and ASW sweeps. VB-127 had the distinction of sinking two U-boats in two different parts of the world, U-591 going down on 30 July 1943 off Recife, in Brazil, and U-761 being claimed on 24 February 1944 off Gibraltar. This aircraft has the Scheme II anti-submarine camouflage, comprising Gull Grey uppersurfaces, non-specular sides and gloss white undersurfaces.

10
PV-1 BuNo 48832 of VPB-128, the Philippines, 1945
This aircraft displays the last three digits of its BuNo on the tail. Under the nose is the chin package of 0.50-cal machine guns that replaced the bombardier's station. VB-128 served in the Atlantic theatre until reforming for duty in the Pacific in January 1945.

11
PV-1 'Black 129-B-3' (BuNo unknown) of VPB-129, Bahia, Brazil, 1943
To eliminate the presence of U-boats in the Caribbean and South Atlantic, PV-1 units were stationed in Florida, Cuba, Puerto Rico, Trinidad and Brazil from 1943 until war's end. Here, they flew ASW patrols under the control of FAW-12 and -16. This aircraft features a unit identification number, which was a popular style of marking amongst eastern seaboard PV-1 units. The PV-1 also has the last digit of its in-squadron serial number painted onto the engine nacelle.

12
PV-1 'Black 132-B-1' (BuNo unknown) flown by Lt Tidmarsh, VB-132, Port Lyautey, French Morocco, 1944
Early PV-1s were adorned with Disney characters and patriotic slogans, which were usually painted on the rear fuselage. This aircraft features the character *Thumper* from the film *Bambi* on its rear fuselage. Other Venturas were adorned with art based on individual crew preferences. VB-132 was responsible for training the first Free French PV-1 Squadron (VFP-1) while stationed at Port Lyautey.

13
PV-1 BuNo 48891 flown by Lt M A 'Butch' Mason, Executive Officer, VB-135, Attu, Alaska, May 1944
On 12 June 1944 Lt M A 'Butch' Mason led six Venturas on a bombing mission against a newly discovered airfield on Shimushu, in the northern Kurile Islands. Coming in at low level, the bombers knocked out the airfield with 500-lb general-purpose bombs, before returning safely to Attu. This aircraft's in-squadron number appears above the national insignia on both sides of the aircraft, while the last three digits of its BuNo adorn the rear fuselage. BuNo 48891 may have also had the FAW-4 insignia applied at a later date. Transferred to VPB-136, it was eventually lost on 17 March 1945 when its crew was forced to ditch three miles off Kodiak, in Alaska. The crew climbed into a life raft and paddled ashore.

14
PV-1 BuNo 34991 of VPB-150, Tarawa, 1944–45
Nicknamed the 'Devilfish P-Viators', VPB-150 operated from Tarawa and Tinian in the Central Pacific between July 1944 and March 1945. It adorned all of its PV-1s with this distinctive rendering of an octopus. This particular aircraft later flew with VPB-133, and it features the last three digits of its bureau number on the forward and rear fuselage.

15
PV-1 BuNo 49418 flown by Crew 4, VPB-151, Tinian, Mariana Islands, 1944–45
VPB-151 was another Central Pacific-based PV-1 squadron, flying from Tinian, in the Mariana Islands, between August 1944 and June 1945. The crew of this aircraft consisted of Clarence 'Tuffy' Thompson, Ross Shadinger, Lloyd Mattingly, Harlan Cooper, John Snee and 'Andy' Anderson.

16
PV-1 BuNo 33253 flown by Capt J H Wehman, VMF(N)-531, Russell and Treasury Islands, South Pacific, February 1944

The US Marines Corps used the PV-1 as a night-fighter between October 1943 and June 1944. Based in the Russell and Treasury Islands, the VMF(N)-531 shot down 12 enemy aircraft. Installed in *C's* nose is the AI Mk IV radar antenna. On 9 February 1944, BuNo 33253's landing gear collapsed on landing at Green Island and the Ventura was written off.

17
PV-1 2195 of No 149 Sqn, Prince Rupert, British Columbia, 1943
This aircraft was one of 286 Venturas that equipped five RCAF squadrons. This particular example served with No 149 Sqn at Prince Rupert, in British Columbia, flying ASW patrols. It has its single letter squadron code both on the rear and forward fuselage. After the war, 2195 was bought by Spartan Air Services and converted into a photographic survey platform. On 14 August 1953 it crash-landed in muskeg some 50 miles from Yellowknife, and here it stayed for a further 35 years. In 1988 the aircraft was recovered from the muskeg by the Ventura Memorial Foundation of Edmonton, Canada, where it is now undergoing restoration.

18
PV-1 NZ4503 (ex-BuNo 33309) of No 1 Sqn, Whenuapi, New Zealand, June 1943
This PV-1 arrived on 7 June 1943 at Whenuapi and became the first of its type to enter service with the RNZAF. Sporting a standard US Navy two-tone paint scheme of blue-grey uppersurfaces and light grey undersurfaces, NZ4503 was adorned with a type 'C' RAF roundel and RNZAF serial number on the rear fuselage. The small red dot in the roundel was briefly worn in the summer of 1943, but it was soon replaced by a larger RNZAF blue circle. NZ4503 was sold for scrap in 1948.

19
PV-1 NZ4633 (ex-BuNo 49579) of No 3 Sqn, Green Island, South Pacific, April 1945
No 3 Sqn flew from Green Island between March and June 1945, during which time its principal mission was the harassment of Japanese troops on Bougainville and New Ireland. NZ4633 arrived in New Zealand on 15 June 1943 in the standard US Navy scheme – sea-blue uppersurfaces, intermediate sides and light grey/non-specular white undersurfaces. The last two digits of its serial number appear on the tail. When serving in operational areas, RNZAF Venturas had white bars added to their roundels.

20
PV-1 NZ4525 (ex-BuNo 34678) of No 2 Sqn, Henderson Field, Guadalcanal, September 1943
Ventura NZ4525 arrived in New Zealand on 10 August 1943, adorned with a *Donald Duck* cartoon on its rear fuselage. As can be seen, this was crudely painted over, for senior commanders within the RNZAF believed that a crew shot down and captured would stand a better chance of survival if their aircraft did not display anti-Japanese art.

21
PV-1 'White 34' of No 1 Bombing Operational Training Unit, Ohakea, New Zealand, 1945
No 1 BTU was assigned the task of training crews for all bomber reconnaissance squadrons. Based at Ohakea, the unit performed this function until June 1945, when it began training transport crews.

22
PV-1 NZ4516 (ex-BuNo 33440) flown by Flt Lt Spicer, No 1 Sqn, Henderson Field, Guadalcanal, December 1943
This aircraft was marked with the titling *PATUA TE RA* (Maori for Striking the Sun) on its nose. It seems that RNZAF PV-1s were not the property of individual squadrons, being controlled instead by Servicing Units which 'loaned out' aircraft on an as needed basis.

23
PV-1 A59-61 of No 13 Sqn, Gove, Northern Territory, 1944-45
The RAAF was issued with some 75 Venturas, whose aircraft numbers ranged from A59-1 through to A59-104. Most of these served with No 13 Sqn at some stage in the air force careers. This particular aircraft was received by the unit on 29 April 1944 and has the squadron code letters 'SF' painted on the fuselage – the individual letter 'Y' was applied later on. Surviving the war, it was disposed of in 1946–47.

24
Ventura Mk II AE939 of No 464 Sqn, Feltwell, December 1942
This aircraft served with No 464 Sqn from December 1942 through to November 1943. Along with Ventura AJ174, AE939 achieved the highest number of sorties with 19. This aircraft, like her sisters, was passed on to meteorological and training units in August 1943.

25
Ventura GR V JT894 of No 521 Sqn, Docking, 1943–44
The Ventura GR V was the British equivalent of the US Navy's PV-1. After serving with No 2 Group, most Venturas were assigned to Coastal Command, Meteorological Squadrons or Operational Training Units. No 521 Sqn flew Venturas from October 1943 through to December 1944.

26
Ventura GR V JS403 of No 22 Sqn, Italy, June 1944
The South African Air Force received 134 Venturas, some of which it operated into the 1960s. JS403 served with No 22 Sqn in the Mediterranean, where it was primarily used escorting convoys and dropping surrender leaflets.

27
PV-1 of the *1° Grupo de Bombardeio Médio*, Recife, Brazil, 1945

The Brazilian air force was founded in 1941, and commenced neutrality patrols with aircraft obtained from the United States. On 22 August 1942, Brazil declared war on both Germany and Italy after a number of its merchant ships had been sunk by U-boats. The Brazilian air force received 16 PV-1s, with the first arriving on 30 March 1944. A year earlier, the United States-Brazilian Unit (UsBaTu) had been formed to train Brazilian military personnel in the art of ASW. After training, the aircraft and crews were assigned to the No 1 Medium Bomber Group at Recife. By then, however, there were no more U-boats operating in Brazilian waters. This aircraft displays standard US Navy type II anti-submarine camouflage.

28
PV-2 BuNo 37101 of VPB-142/153, NAS Kaneohe, Hawaii, May 1945

The PV-2s of VPB-142 had an APA-16 radar bombsight installed, which improved night attacks against Japanese-held islands in the Central Pacific. This aircraft was being used by VPB-153 when it crashed on a night take-off from Kaneohe on 5 May 1945. Its five-man crew were killed.

29
PV-2 'Black 24' (BuNo unknown) of VPB-139, flown by Lt Alfred 'Fritz' Daniel, Attu Island, Alaska, March 1945

VPB-139 became the first squadron to operate the PV-2 Harpoon when it went into action in March 1945, performing rocket, bombing and strafing attacks against Japanese targets in the Northern Kurile Islands. Aside from 'Fritz' Daniel, the rest of the crew of this PV-2 consisted of co-pilot Gerald 'Gerry' Russello, Navigator William 'Bill' Simms, Mechanic (AMM1/c) Blaine Edward 'Blackie' Ore, Radio/Radarman (ARM1/c) William 'Bill' L Gorrell and Ordnanceman (AOM2/c) John Medlock. The small oval window below the national insignia had several uses. Many times it was used as a gun port for a 0.30-cal machine gun or a 0.45-cal Thompson machine gun loaded with a lot of tracer, which proved effective in getting enemy fighters to move away from the PV-2 so that the Martin turret or dorsal gunners could get a shot. Additionally, it was used as an observation port for checking waves, determining wind direction and velocity. A second port on the starboard underside was used for trailing a wire antenna for the radio transmitter.

30
PV-2 BuNo 37474 of VPB-148, FAW-2, NAS Kaneohe, Hawaii, June 1945

VPB-148 was equipped with 15 PV-2s when it arrived at Kaneohe, and detachments conducted ASW patrols from Johnson and Midway Islands during the final days of the war. This aircraft has its serial numbers marked in yellow, while PV-1 units usually applied them in black or white.

SELECTED BIBLIOGRAPHY

Books

Bowyer, Michael J F. *2 Group RAF: A Complete History, 1936–1945*. Crecy Books, 1992

Carey, Alan C. *Above an Angry Sea: United States Navy B-24 Liberator and PB4Y-2 Privateer Operations in the Pacific*. Schiffer Publishing, Ltd, 2001

Grantham, Sid. *The 13 Squadron Story*. The 13 Squadron 50th Anniversary Fund, Dee Why, New South Wales, 1991

Ross, J M S. *Official History of Royal New Zealand Air Force*. Battery Press, 1993

Sanford, Kenneth E. *Crew Six*. Sanford Publishing Group, 1996

Scrivner, Charles L. *The Empire Express*. Historical Aviation Album Series. Historical Aviation Album, Temple City, CA

Scrivner, Charles L and Captain W E Scarborough, USN (ret). *Lockheed PV-1 Ventura in Action*. Squadron/Signal Publications Inc, 1981

Sherrod, Robert. *History of Marine Corps Aviation in World War II*. Combat Forces Press: Washington, DC, 1952

Stanaway, John C. *Vega Ventura: The Operational History of Lockheed's Lucky Star*. Schiffer Publishing, 1996

Government Sources

Dictionary of American Naval Aviation Squadrons, Vol 2. Naval Aviation History Office, Washington, DC

After Action Reports and Squadron Histories of USN and USMC VB and VPB Squadrons located at the National Archives in College Park, Maryland

Periodicals

'Pacific Venturas', *FlyPast* Magazine, September 1993, pgs 34–35

'Pacific Venturas', *FlyPast* Magazine, October 1993, pgs 73–77

'Ventura', *Naval Aviation News*, August 1974, pgs 20–21

'VPB-123', *Naval Aviation News*, March 1948, pg 16

INDEX

References to illustrations are shown in **bold**. Plates are shown with page and caption locators in brackets.